THE WORLD OF 5G

Volume 3

INTELLIGENT HOME

THE WORLD OF 5G
(In 5 Volumes)

5G的世界 — 万物互联
Originally published in Chinese by Guangdong Science and Technology Press Co., Ltd.
Copyright © Guangdong Science and Technology Press Co., Ltd. 2020

The World of 5G — Internet of Everything, Vol. 1
Copyright © 2022 by World Scientific Publishing Co. Pte. Ltd.

5G的世界 — 智能制造
Originally published in Chinese by Guangdong Science and Technology Press Co., Ltd.
Copyright © Guangdong Science and Technology Press Co., Ltd. 2020

The World of 5G — Intelligent Manufacturing, Vol. 2
Copyright © 2022 by World Scientific Publishing Co. Pte. Ltd.

5G的世界 — 智能家居
Originally published in Chinese by Guangdong Science and Technology Press Co., Ltd.
Copyright © Guangdong Science and Technology Press Co., Ltd. 2020

The World of 5G — Intelligent Home, Vol. 3
Copyright © 2022 by World Scientific Publishing Co. Pte. Ltd.

5G的世界 — 智慧交通
Originally published in Chinese by Guangdong Science and Technology Press Co., Ltd.
Copyright © Guangdong Science and Technology Press Co., Ltd. 2020

The World of 5G — Intelligent Transportation, Vol. 4
Copyright © 2022 by World Scientific Publishing Co. Pte. Ltd.

5G的世界 — 智慧医疗
Originally published in Chinese by Guangdong Science and Technology Press Co., Ltd.
Copyright © Guangdong Science and Technology Press Co., Ltd. 2020

The World of 5G — Intelligent Medicine, Vol. 5
Copyright © 2022 by World Scientific Publishing Co. Pte. Ltd.

THE WORLD OF 5G

Volume 3

INTELLIGENT HOME

Wei Wu
Skyworth Group Co., Ltd., China

Translator
Wenjia Han
Yimei (Beijing) Technology Co., Ltd.

Proofreader
Lianghe Dong
Mudanjiang Normal University, China

NEW JERSEY · LONDON · SINGAPORE · BEIJING · SHANGHAI · HONG KONG · TAIPEI · CHENNAI · TOKYO

Published by

World Scientific Publishing Co. Pte. Ltd.
5 Toh Tuck Link, Singapore 596224
USA office: 27 Warren Street, Suite 401-402, Hackensack, NJ 07601
UK office: 57 Shelton Street, Covent Garden, London WC2H 9HE

Library of Congress Cataloging-in-Publication Data
Names: Xue, Quan (Telecommunications professor), editor-in-chief.
Title: The world of 5G / authors, Quan Xue, South China University of Technology, China,
  Wenquan Che, South China University of Technology, China, Jishun Guo,
  Joyson Intelligent Automotive Research Institute, China, Wei Wu, Skyworth Group Co., Ltd., China,
  Zhiqiang Xu, Guangzhou Hantele Communication Co., Ltd., China, Wenhua Huang,
  Southern Medical University, China, Haibin Lin, Affiliated Hospital of Putian University, China.
Description: Singapore ; Hackensack, NJ : World Scientific Publishing Co. Pte. Ltd, [2022] |
  Includes bibliographical references and index. | Contents: v. 1. Internet of everything --
  v. 2. Intelligent manufacturing -- v. 3. Intelligent home -- v. 4. Intelligent transportation --
  v. 5. Intelligent medicine.
Identifiers: LCCN 2021061659 | ISBN 9789811250170 (set ; hardcover) | ISBN 9789811250187
  (set ; ebook for institutions) | ISBN 9789811250194 (set ; ebook for individuals) |
  ISBN 9789811244131 (v. 1 ; hardcover) | ISBN 9789811244148 (v. 1 ; ebook for institutions) |
  ISBN 9789811244155 (v. 1 ; ebook for individuals) | ISBN 9789811244223 (v. 2 ; hardcover) |
  ISBN 9789811244230 (v. 2 ; ebook for institutions) | ISBN 9789811244247 (v. 2 ; ebook for individuals) |
  ISBN 9789811244254 (v. 3 ; hardcover) | ISBN 9789811244261 (v. 3 ; ebook for institutions) |
  ISBN 9789811244278 (v. 3 ; ebook for individuals) | ISBN 9789811244162 (v. 4 ; hardcover) |
  ISBN 9789811244179 (v. 4 ; ebook for institutions | ISBN 9789811244186 (v. 4 ; ebook for individuals) |
  ISBN 9789811244193 (v. 5 ; hardcover) | ISBN 9789811244209 (v. 5 ; ebook for institutions) |
  ISBN 9789811244216 (v. 5 ; ebook for individuals)
Subjects: LCSH: 5G mobile communication systems. | Expert systems (Computer science) | Automation.
Classification: LCC TK5103.25 .X84 2022 | DDC 621.3845/6--dc23/eng/20220224
LC record available at https://lccn.loc.gov/2021061659

British Library Cataloguing-in-Publication Data
A catalogue record for this book is available from the British Library.

Copyright © 2022 by World Scientific Publishing Co. Pte. Ltd.

All rights reserved. This book, or parts thereof, may not be reproduced in any form or by any means, electronic or mechanical, including photocopying, recording or any information storage and retrieval system now known or to be invented, without written permission from the publisher.

For photocopying of material in this volume, please pay a copying fee through the Copyright Clearance Center, Inc., 222 Rosewood Drive, Danvers, MA 01923, USA. In this case permission to photocopy is not required from the publisher.

For any available supplementary material, please visit
https://www.worldscientific.com/worldscibooks/10.1142/12479#t=suppl

Printed in Singapore

Foreword
5G Empowers the Society
for Development at a Rapid Speed

Being one of the buzzwords of the global media in recent years, 5G is very attractive because it carries great expectations from people, both in terms of the communication technology itself and the industry changes it could unleash. Recalling the development of human society, technological change is undoubtedly one of the biggest engines. Marked by the invention of the steam engine and electricity, the first two Industrial Revolutions featured mechanization and electrification, respectively. As the wheel of history rolls into the 21st century, a new round of Industrial Revolution featuring intelligence will be looming, and its impact on human civilization and economic development will be no less than that of the previous two Industrial Revolutions. But then what is pushing it? Compared with the previous two, the new Industrial Revolution is no longer pushed by a single technology but instead by the integration of multiple technologies, among which mobile communication, Internet, artificial intelligence, and biotechnology are the decisive elements.

5G, as the commanding heights of modern mobile technology, is an important engine that enables other key technologies mentioned above. Meanwhile, it can also be seen that 5G comes out when the new momentum is needed most by the Internet development. After almost linear rapid growth, the increment rate of China's Internet users is falling with the popularity rate of mobile phones almost refusing to grow. Owning to the fast pace of life, the netizens now pursue new forms of business with short periods, low investments, and quick returns. Faster speed and lower fees have mitigated the cost pressure on broadband Internet access when short videos and small programs are becoming popular. But these are still not enough to meet the requirements of the new format of the Internet. The future development of the Internet calls for new drivers and new models to solve this problem. The industrial Internet, regarded as the second half of the Internet, has just started, and its new driving forces cannot fill deficiencies of the consumer Internet driving force. At present, the Internet enters into a transition period of continuity for new drivers to replace the old ones. At a time when the consumption of the Internet needs to be intensified and the industrial Internet is starting to take off, 5G comes into being.

As the latest generation of cellular mobile communication technology, 5G is characterized by high speed, low latency, wide connectivity, and high reliability. Compared with 4G, 5G's peak rate increases by 30 times, user experience rate advances by 10 times, and spectrum efficiency accelerates by three times. Moreover, compared to 4G, 5G mobile supports high-speed rail with the speed of 500 km/h, with its wireless interface delay reduced by 90%, the connection density enhanced by 10 times, energy efficiency and traffic density improved by 100 times, enough to support the mobile Internet industry and many applications of the Internet. Compared with the previous four generations of mobile communication technologies, the most important change in 5G is the shift from individual-oriented use to industry-oriented applications, providing indispensable high-speed, massive, and low-latency connectivity for Internet of Everything needed by the new round of Industrial Revolution. Therefore, 5G is not only merely a communication technology but also an important "infrastructure".

It is well timed and also quite accountable in cultural inheritance for Guangdong Science and Technology Publishing House to take the lead in organizing the compilation and distribution of this book series and to popularize 5G knowledge in the society for improving the national scientific literacy when the whole society is talking about 5G with great expectations. Compared with the numerous books about 5G in the market, this series stands out with its own characteristics. First of all, Professor Xue Quan, the Chief Editor, who has been focusing on the research of 5G cutting-edge core technologies in recent years, is an expert in the fields of millimeter wave and terahertz. He took the lead in the compilation of this series with his team responsible for the volume, *5G Internet of*

Everything, thus aiming to well leverage the tool for the popularization of science to present 5G technology mass-orientally. In addition, with the focus on the integration and application of 5G in the vertical industry, the series comes out just in line with the close social concerns about 5G. The team included industry experts from the Guangdong Provincial Key Laboratory of Millimeter Wave and Terahertz in the South China University of Technology, Automotive Engineering Research Institute of Guangzhou Automobile Group Co., Ltd., Southern Medical University, Guangzhou Hanxin Communication Technology Co., Ltd., Skyworth Group Co., Ltd., for the corresponding volume, respectively. This book series is targeted at the current pain points of the industry, yet contributes to an unfettered imagination of the future of the 5G-enabling industry. It will be an invaluable science book for the public yearning for new technology for a new round of industrial transformation. The first issue of the book series consists of five volumes.

What's remarkable is that while the book focuses on how 5G will revolutionize the vertical industry if integrated with other technologies, it also explores the possible negative effects of technological advances on human beings. In the progress of science and technology, it is essential to stick to human nature, ethics, morality, and law. So the acceleration of the development of science and technology, with "safety valve" and "brake" being indispensable, shouldn't be based on the sacrifice of the dominance of human nature and the thinking ability of human beings. We need to think of science and technology as a "double-edged sword" and better exploit the advantages and avoid disadvantages while turning the passive reaction into an active response.

Coming in with a roar, 5G will have an immeasurable impact on the development of human society. Let's work together and march toward the future.

Wu Hequan
Member of Chinese Academy of Engineering

Foreword
5G as the Engine for Upgrading and Development of the Vertical Industries

As we all know, we are gradually entering a digital era, and many industries and technologies will progress around the data chain, in which the main effect of mobile communication technology is data transmission. Applications that require performance such as high-definition video, multi-device access, and real-time two-way interaction between multiple people are difficult to achieve without the support of high-speed communication technology. As the latest generation of cellular mobile communication technology, 5G features high speed, low delay, wide connection, and high reliability.

The year 2020 marks the first year for 5G commercial use and then the employment of 5G is expected to peak around 2035. 5G will be mainly applied in the following seven fields: smart creation, smart city, smart grid, smart office, smart security, telemedicine and health care, and commercial retail. In these seven fields, it is estimated that nearly 50% of 5G components will be applied to smart creation, while nearly 18.7% will be applied to smart city construction.

The importance of 5G is not only reflected in its great promotion of upgrading industries such as smart creation but also reflected in its direct correlation with the development of artificial intelligence. The development of artificial intelligence requires a large number of user cases and data, and the amount of data that 4G Internet of Things can provide for learning is incomparable to that of 5G. Therefore, the development of 5G

Internet of Things plays a very important role in promoting the development of artificial intelligence. Relying on 5G can help promote the upgrading of many vertical industries. It is also for this reason that 5G's leading development has become an important engine to promote the development of national science and technology and economy and has also become the focus of competition between China and the United States in the field of science and technology.

Against this background, Guangdong Science and Technology Publishing House took the lead in organizing the compilation and distribution of the "5G World" book series, with the focus on the integrated application and empowerment of 5G in many industries, including manufacturing, medical care, transportation, home furniture, finance, education, and so on. On the one hand, it is a courageous and culturally responsible measure to popularize 5G among the public, enhancing national scientific literacy. On the other hand, this book is also an utterly precious reference for industry insiders who want to understand the trend for the development of 5G technology and industrial integration.

This book series was done under the guidance of Chief Editor, Professor Xue Quan, the Director of the Guangdong Key Laboratory of Millimeter Wave and Terahertz, South China University of Technology. As an expert in the fields of millimeter wave and terahertz technology, Professor Xue Quan will manage to make a book series of popular science with accurate and natural technical features. This book series is scheduled to be publish the first editions of five volumes, including *The World of 5G: Internet of Everything, The World of 5G: Intelligent Manufacturing, The World of 5G: Intelligent Home, The World of 5G: Intelligent Transportation,* and *The World of 5G: Intelligent Medicine*. The compilation team of this series boasts of strong support. In addition to *The World of 5G: Internet of Everything*, which was written by the technical team of Guangdong Millimeter Wave and Terahertz Key Laboratory of South China University of Technology, the other four volumes were mainly written by relevant industry experts. Among all the volumes, *The World of 5G: Intelligent Manufacturing* was written by experts from the Auto Engineering Research Institute of Guangzhou Automobile Group Co., Ltd., while *The World of 5G: Intelligent Medicine* was written by experts from Southern Medical University. *The World of 5G: Intelligent Transportation* was written by Guangzhou Hantele Communication Co., Ltd., and *The World of 5G: Intelligent Home* was written by Skyworth Group Co., Ltd. This kind of cross-industry combination writing team possesses a strong complementary and professional system for the following reasons: for one thing, technical experts can fully grasp the evolution of mobile communication technology and key technologies of 5G; for another, industry experts can accurately feel the pain points of the industry as well as analyze the advantages and challenges of the industries integrated with 5G through incise writing around the central themes to provide a valuable reference for industry peers with real and vivid cases.

Besides a vivid description of the huge changes that could be brought about by the 5G technology merged into industries, what makes this book novel and fresh is the fact that they also discuss the negative effects the rapid advance of technology may have on human beings. The rapid development of high technology should not be done at the cost of human nature, ethics, and thoughts. It is necessary to make sure that technology conforms to science and ethics with the essential "cushion" and "safety valve".

Mao Junfa
Member of Chinese Academy of Sciences

Preface

As a revolutionary leap in technology, 5G provides Internet of Everything with important technical support. Furthermore, it will bring prosperity for mobile Internet and industrial Internet and provide many industries with unprecedented opportunities, thus being expected to trigger profound changes in the whole society. What is 5G? How will 5G empower various industries and promote a new round of Industrial Revolution? The answers can be found in the series *The World of 5G*, which consists of five volumes.

The volume *The World of 5G: Internet of Everything* is edited by Xue Quan, Director of Guangdong Key Laboratory of Millimeter Wave and Terahertz, South China University of Technology, and mainly expounds the iterative development history of mobile communication technology, the characteristics and limitations of the first four generations of mobile communication technology, the technical characteristics of 5G and its possible industrial application prospects, and the development trend of mobile communication technology in the post-5G era. By reading this volume, the reader can obtain a carefully and skillfully drawn picture of the past, present, and future applications of 5G.

The volume *The World of 5G: Intelligent Manufacturing* is edited by Dr. Guo Jishun of Automotive Engineering Research Institute of Guangzhou Automobile Group Co., Ltd., and mainly introduces the development process of the Industrial Revolution, the opportunity brought about by 5G to the manufacturing industry, the upgrade of smart creation assisted by 5G, and the application of intelligent production based on 5G. Through this volume, readers can understand the opportunities for the transformation of traditional manufacturing produced by 5G+ smart creation and learn by experience what kind of revolution manufacturing innovation will create in the society.

The volume *The World of 5G: Intelligent Home* is edited by Wu Wei from Skyworth Group Co., Ltd., and mainly elaborates on the evolution of smart home, the key technologies that 5G uses to facilitate the intelligent development of home life, as well as innovative smart home products based on 5G technology. Home furnishing is closely tied to our daily life. By reading this volume, readers can understand the convenience and comfort arising from the integration of 5G and smart home. It provides a glimpse of the wonderful life that technology has created.

The volume *The World of 5G: Intelligent Transportation* is edited by Xu Zhiqiang from Guangzhou Hexin Communications Technology Co., Ltd., and mainly describes the development process of smart transportation, the key 5G technologies and architectures used in smart transportation, as well as the application examples of smart transportation based on 5G. By reading this volume, readers can be fully informed about the future development trend of smart transportation led by 5G technology.

The volume *The Word of 5G: Intelligent Medicine* is edited by Huang Wenhua and Lin Haibin from Southern Medical University, and mainly focuses on the effect of the integration of 5G and medical treatment, including the advantages of smart medicine compared with traditional medical treatment, how 5G promotes the development of smart medicine and smart medicine terminals and new medical applications integrated with 5G. Reading between the lines, readers can gain a comprehensive understanding of the huge application potential of 5G technology in the medical industry and be keenly aware of the well-being that technological progress has contributed to human health.

Finally, we specially acknowledge the funding from projects such as prior research and development projects "Key Technology of Millimeter Wave Integrated RF Front-end System Compatible with C Band (2018YFB1802000)" of the National Ministry of Science and Technology, the major science and technology project of "Research on 5G Millimeter Wave Broadband High Efficiency Chip and Phased Array System (2018B010115001)" of Guangdong Science and Technology Department, and Strategic Consulting Project of "Guangdong New Generation Information Technology Development Strategy Research (201816611292)" of Guangdong Research Institute of Chinese Academy of Engineering Development Strategy.

5G brings us technological change, industry upgrade, and social upheaval with unprecedented speed and strength, while also generating great challenges. Let's navigate our way ahead while harnessing the waves of 5G.

About the Author

Wei Wu is the Chief Engineer and Professor-level Senior Engineer of Skyworth Group. He is also a Member of the Electronic Science and Technology Committee of the Ministry of Industry and Information Technology, a Member of the National Audio and Video Standardization Technical Committee, and the Director of the Guangdong Ultra-High Definition Display Engineering Technology Research Center.

He once presided over the projects of core electronics, high-end general chips, and infrastructural software projects, and the intelligent manufacturing project of the Ministry of Industry and Information Technology. He has won the Guangdong and Shenzhen Science and Technology Progress Award eight times and has also won the first prize of the National Science and Technology Progress Award on behalf of the enterprise.

Contents

Foreword: 5G Empowers the Society for Development at a Rapid Speed   v

Foreword: 5G as the Engine for Upgrading and Development of the Vertical Industries   ix

Preface   xiii

About the Author   xvii

Chapter 1 The Past and Present of Smart Home   1
  1.1 The Evolution of Smart Home   1
    1.1.1 Smart home — being around us for a decade   1
    1.1.2 The nature of smart home   3
  1.2 When Smart Home Meets 5G   5
    1.2.1 The core technology of smart home   5
    1.2.2 The product form of smart home   20

Chapter 2 The Foundation of the Integration of Smart Home and 5G   29
  2.1 Manufacturing Basis: Great Oaks Grow from Little Acorns   29
    2.1.1 The current situation of manufacturing of a smart home   29
    2.1.2 A new manufacturing model for 5G+ industrial Internet   32
    2.1.3 The application scene landing under the new mode   35

xx *The World of 5G: Intelligent Home*

    2.2 Network Foundation: Let the Smart Home be Capable of Connecting Everything   39
        2.2.1 Home network for smart home   39
        2.2.2 Smart home gateway in the 5G era   43
    2.3 System Foundation: A Unified Platform Based on 5G + Four System Technologies   47
        2.3.1 System architecture   48
        2.3.2 Design of a terminal operating system   48
        2.3.3 Design of equipment access network system   51
        2.3.4 Design of data system   52
        2.3.5 Design of the artificial intelligence algorithm system   53
    2.4 Business Model Basis: New Home Furnishing Business Form in the 5G Environment   54
        2.4.1 5G+ smart real estate   54
        2.4.2 5G+ smart new retail   58

Chapter 3 Typical Applications of Smart Home–5G Integration   63
    3.1 5G+ Ultra-high Definition (UHD) Television   63
        3.1.1 Development trend of flat-panel TV   63
        3.1.2 Implementation plan of 5G + 8K smart TV   65
    3.2 5G + VR/AR   69
        3.2.1 The concept and evolution of VR/AR   69
        3.2.2 Technological innovations that 5G brings to VR/AR   72
        3.2.3 The future model of VR/AR in smart homes   74
    3.3 5G + Home Security   74
        3.3.1 The origin and development of home security   75
        3.3.2 Home security applications and products   75
    3.4 5G + Home Network Equipment   78
        3.4.1 The development process of home networking devices   78
        3.4.2 Deficiencies in today's home networking devices   79
        3.4.3 5G CPE realizes all-region coverage of home network   80
    3.5 5G + Set-Top Box (STB)   84
        3.5.1 The origin and development of STB   84
        3.5.2 The coverage dead zone of STB   86
        3.5.3 Smart STB will be everywhere with the help of 5G   86

3.6 5G + AIoT   90
   3.6.1 AIoT: From IoT   90
   3.6.2 AIoT: The future of intelligence of everything   92
   3.6.3 Three applications of 5G and AIoT   94

**Chapter 4 Innovative Products Integrating Smart
            Home and 5G**   **99**
   4.1 Intelligent Home System   99
      4.1.1 A new definition of the 5G smart home system   99
      4.1.2 Architecture scheme of the intelligent home system   100
      4.1.3 Composition analysis of the intelligent home system   103
      4.1.4 New interactive experience of the smart home
             system   106
   4.2 Intelligent Control Center   111
      4.2.1 New demand for 5G intelligent control center   111
      4.2.2 Intelligent control center with a fixed form   113
      4.2.3 Intelligent control center with a mobile form   120
      4.2.4 The future of the intelligent control center system   122

Bibliography   125

Index   129

Chapter 1

The Past and Present of Smart Home

1.1 The Evolution of Smart Home

1.1.1 *Smart home — being around us for a decade*

At the 1933 Chicago World's Fair, "Alpha", a robot, introduced the concept of home automation to the public, marking the first introduction of the smart home under the name, "House of Tomorrow". Later, in 1950, American mechanical genius Emil Mathias turned his home into a "Push Button Manor" by using mechanical tools, turning the physical smart home into a reality for the first time. He also proposed the concept of full coverage smart home. In 1957, to further develop the smart home and help people understand this concept, Monsanto and Disney jointly proposed the idea of building "The Monsanto House of the Future" and then successfully built it. The Xanadu House in Kissimmee, Florida, USA was opened to the public in 1983. The lighting system and security system in the house were all controlled by computers, representing a good start for the early-stage smart home.

Prior to the year 2000, the idea of smart home was in its infancy, and the whole industry was just starting to get familiar with the concept and product. Back then, only a handful of smart home concepts and products were available. Nevertheless, as a result of inadequate technology and limited production capacity, professional smart home manufacturers were absent, and most related products went nowhere.

1.1.1.1 *"Fire sparks" in China's smart home market*

It was not until 2000 that some relatively mature smart products from other countries were introduced into China via a few Chinese agencies. At that time, smart home was poised for take-off. Some domestic businesses seized the opportunities brought about by the rising demand in the smart home market and set up multiple smart home R&D teams and manufacturers in Shenzhen, Hangzhou, Shanghai, and other cities. As businesses dug deeper into such a market, smart home marketing and production technology systems saw gradual improvement in China.

In 2005, the concept of smart home gained popularity in China, and smart home manufacturers embraced the first phase of development. The market segments, including home security system and home smart light control system, were gradually formed and developed. That was the period of exploration in the smart home market. However, due to an imperfect smart home market management system and malicious competition, some businesses overstated what smart home products can do and failed to train the agents, industry users and mass media thus started to question the practicality of a smart home. Meanwhile, limited technical conditions and manufacturers' strength slowed down the smart home market's growth and lowered sales. Consequently, the "fire sparks" that first appeared in China's smart home market gradually went out as sacrifices in the market's barbaric growth.

Until 2008, another development trend emerged in the smart home market. Many well-known brands noticed the once neglected smart home market and focused their efforts on creating an extended smart home product line and related new business segments. Manufacturers began to take interest in smart homes in this period.

1.1.1.2 *Embrace the remarkable development of smart home*

Since 2011, the advancement of Internet of Things (IoT) technology has made more things possible in the smart home industry. Innovative research teams represented by those studying smart single products have been mushrooming, ushering in a period of technological improvement in the field of smart home. As technology advances with healthy competition among various brands, some smart single products were sold in the market at affordable prices, greatly lowering the threshold for ordinary users to experience smart home products. A wide range of applications and the popularization of Wi-Fi also made smart home products easier to use, and the smart home market has been gaining momentum. Therefore, in the new Internet era, the smart home market aiming at improving ease of use has gradually taken shape, and the smart home industry has taken on a new appearance.

The advancement of IoT stimulated the development of the smart home in 2014, and "ecosphere" has emerged as a buzzword in the smart product industry. Moreover, the technical standards and protocols generated during the technological improvement period were interconnected and integrated. On this basis, a growing number of famous companies undertook to build the ecosphere of smart single products. Through systematic thinking, the smart product ecosphere combines smart single items to form a control system that facilitates user management, so that the smart home is no longer fragmented, and systemized, smart home life in different scenarios becomes a reality for better user experience. In this sense, Xiaomi is a leader as it stood out with its ecological chain system, its products' low prices and relatively reliable quality, as well as easy-to-use interactive apps. Xiaomi has become a pioneer in IoT and has won the favor of consumers.

1.1.2 *The nature of smart home*

Upon learning about the evolution of the concepts and products of smart homes, we still need to look into the nature of the smart home before discussing the future prospects of the smart home based on its definition.

Intelligent home, or smart home, refers to the connection of a series of home information-related facilities including home appliances, communication devices, and home safety equipment through network communication, automatic control, and home bus technologies to a home intelligent integrated system that supports information interaction and helps control the household facilities. The smart home aims to realize the automatic control of machines by the system instead of human hands. In this way, home life would be more convenient, safe, and comfortable after getting rid of the household chores. In the meantime, home-related data and information are obtained for processing via the integrated system to intelligently control the running timeframe and power of household appliances, advance the establishment of an energy-saving and eco-friendly living environment, and enable the smart home industry to contribute more to mankind and the entire society.

In terms of automatic control, a smart home can be subdivided into four parts: home automation, home network, network appliances, and information appliances. They contribute to the realization of smart life by working both individually and collectively.

Home automation is essential to a smart home. It analyzes and processes home-related data and information, and the obtained information will be analyzed through microelectronic technology for the integrated control of the lighting system, safety system, temperature control system, and other systems in the house. As a control network, home automation plays a critical role in the smart home system with automatic control as the core technology.

Home network is a technology that connects household appliances to the wide-area network within a household. "Wired" and "wireless" connections are the two main types of connection in home networks. Different from a traditional network, the home network is somewhat special as many product settings and systems that can only be used in a home setting are involved.

Network appliances improve traditional appliances by using advanced technologies, such as digital technology, network technology, and household automatic control technology, and turn them into new household appliances that offer more convenience for people and can be connected to smart home systems.

Information appliances refer to the household appliances that can provide information about the home environment, exchange information, or automatically process environmental information in the smart home system through the network. Like network appliances, information appliances also require communication equipment for connection with smart home systems. Technically speaking, information appliances are network appliances, and televisions, set-top boxes, computers, and other home appliances with similar information processing methods are typical information appliances.

The four parts of the smart home work together to form the overall smart home system, allowing people to lead a more convenient life. The ultimate goal of a home network-based smart home that realizes the interactive operation between network appliances and information appliances is to make people's home life safer, more convenient, and comfortable. Therefore, a smart home system that improves the quality of home life can be designed only by learning about user habits, sharing the information coming from information appliances and realizing the automatic calculation of the changes in human and environmental needs under different circumstances and interactive operation of devices.

1.2 When Smart Home Meets 5G

1.2.1 *The core technology of smart home*

1.2.1.1 *Artificial intelligence*

(1) *The integration of artificial intelligence and 5G upgrades smartness*: Artificial Intelligence (AI) involves reasoning, knowledge representation, planning, learning, natural language processing, perception, movement and control, emotional expression abilities, etc. When AI functions in a smart home, natural language processing, planning, and perception are the most commonly used skills, and the technologies for realizing them have built applications based on speech recognition and face recognition. As 5G approaches, widely connected networks with high speed and low latency will significantly improve the response experience of voice recognition and face recognition in smart home scenarios. For example, the entire extended network chain comprises the front-end collection of an array microphone, the request results in Internet service as well as the third-party service acquisition and interface feedback, in which severe latency has taken place in the transmission of network data. The advent of 5G will improve the experience, and the smart home experience in this scenario will take a giant leap forward.

The concepts, algorithms, and models of AI are changing with each passing day. From the introduction of the concept in the late 1950s to its application in the 21st century, AI has been through the ups and downs of technological tides. AI technology is widely used in the field of smart home, and home-assist robots, natural speech recognition, image recognition, and other AI technologies have brought new changes to modern home life. The promotion of 5G technology will integrate more intriguing scenarios of AI technology application in a household and introduce a "smarter" home life.

In the second decade of the 21st century, the world turned quickly from an era of personal computer (PC) to one of mobility. The development of smartphones and 4G high-speed networks has given birth to a new generation of tools for media and communication, such as

Weibo and WeChat. With the rapid advancement of cloud technology, more individuals and enterprises choose to "upload" their data to the cloud. In an era of Big Data, Google's AlphaGo beat South Korean Go grandmaster Lee Sedol and Chinese Go player Ke Jie in 2016. This highly technical piece of news spread fast via the new media of mobile Internet to all walks of life and has garnered the attention of scientific and technological talents, capital, and governments from all over the world. China has already rolled out national-level AI development policies, as shown in Fig. 1.1. It's fair to say that in recent years, AI technology has been presented with exciting development opportunities at the government, capital, and private levels.

(2) *The integration of artificial intelligence and 5G beefs up smart home development*: With increasingly diversified smart homes and their application scenarios, the number of interconnected smart home devices will explode. Interaction and operation of tons of data require a stable, high-speed, and low-latency network to ensure the best interaction experience for smart devices. However, at present, Wi-Fi, 4G, and other networks could delay by 100 ms, and only a limited number of devices can be connected to Internet of Things (IoT), it will thus be hard for smart devices to further develop. However, these won't be problems anymore with the birth of 5G. 5G has three advantages: high speed, low latency, and large-scale connectivity. 5G supports the interconnection between large-scale smart devices in a small area.

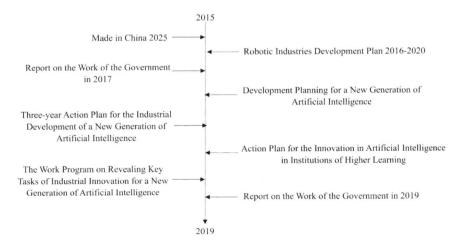

Figure 1.1   China's AI development policies.

Meanwhile, the 5G network enables merely about 10 ms delay in smart devices' voice and image interaction, which is far quicker than that of human response, bringing an excellent experience to users. The high-speed, low-latency 5G makes the interaction between man and smart home simpler and more natural. The integration of AI technology and 5G contributes to a drastic improvement in the interactive technology of the smart home.

The evolution of smart home interaction technology tells us that interacting with the help of AI voice and AI image is the most direct way of communication between men and smart devices. As information technology advances, especially with the advent of the IoT, intelligent speech and image technology have become the most convenient and effective means for information acquisition and communication.

AI-empowered intelligent speech and image technology have become the most important interactive means and usage scenarios in smart homes. As a new way of interaction, intelligent speech and image technology will become an indispensable part of future families. The involvement of AI voice and AI image in the design and development of TV — a major home appliance in the living room — will undoubtedly make the smart home more convenient.

(3) *The key technologies for the interaction between artificial intelligence and smart home*: The key technologies for the interaction between AI and smart home include AI intelligent speech technology and AI image interaction technology:
   (i) *AI intelligent speech technology*: What is intelligent speech technology? To put it simply, it is the conversation between people and things; professionally, it is the communication of man–machine language, which involves speech recognition and speech synthesis technologies. Voice assistants exemplify AI applications. As voice recognition technology develops, more and more electronic products are equipped with voice assistants. Intelligent speech technology has already been widely used in TV products. As the intelligent control center in a house, the TV needs to be able to be controlled at all times. The full-time AI voice interaction technology enables the TV (on or in standby mode) to receive voice control commands and helps the users to control.

   The full-time AI voice interaction technology for the TV requires sound collection based on a built-in audio acquisition module without the use of voice remote control, and AI voice

8 *The World of 5G: Intelligent Home*

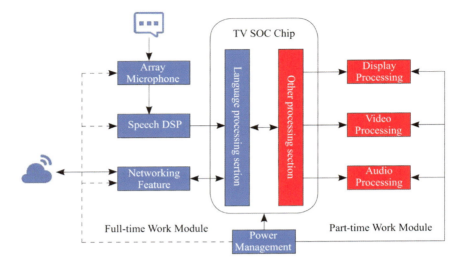

Figure 1.2 The framework of the full-time AI system for the TV.

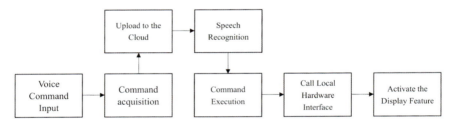

Figure 1.3 The process for realizing full-time AI voice interaction.

interaction can be realized when the TV is turned on or switched to standby mode. The framework of the full-time AI system for the TV is shown in Fig. 1.2.

Figure 1.3 shows the process for realizing full-time AI voice interaction. When the TV is in AI standby mode, after the array microphone receives the voice command of "I want to watch a movie", it realizes sound simulation and digital shift through the TV Central Processing Unit (CPU) before being encapsulated into a data package and uploaded to the speech recognition server on the cloud. The cloud computing-based semantic

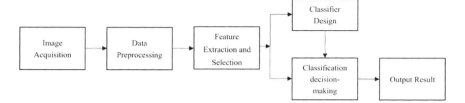

Figure 1.4   Flow diagram of AI image interaction technology.

recognition technology parses the data packages into voice commands and sends them back to the TV. Then, the TV calls the local hardware interface, activates the display feature, and enters the play mode.

(ii) *AI image interaction technology*: AI image interaction technology uses computers to process, analyze, and understand images for the identification of targets and objects in different modes. Figure 1.4 shows how it works. The various steps utilized in this process can be described as follows:

(a) *Image acquisition*: The information of the objects yet to be recognized need to be put into the computer by multiple input devices for the computer to classify and recognize different situations. Then, a matrix or vector is used to represent the information of the objects in question after measurement, sampling, and quantization.

(b) *Data preprocessing*: Noise should be removed, useful information should be stressed, and the degradation caused by input and measuring instruments or other factors should be undone.

(c) *Feature extraction and selection*: Since there might be a large volume of objects to be recognized, the original data has to change in some way for more effective classification and recognition so as to identify the characteristics that best reflect the nature of the classification.

(d) *Classification decision-making*: The computer should be trained with the obtained information for AI, and criteria should be set out to classify those objects in a certain category.

(e) *Classifier design*: The classifier must first be trained and taught before they are able to work effectively. It is particularly important to study the automatic recognition of the machine and train the classifier to perform automatic recognition.

(f) *Output result*: The TV takes screenshots through the camera, and the AI image recognition technology recognizes what is on the image and responds accordingly. For example, when the built-in smart camera captures a picture featuring the elderly and children, the TV will, with the help of AI image recognition technology, automatically adjust the brightness and volume of the screen and customize the audio-visual mode for them.

1.2.1.2 *5G data acquisition technology*

Data acquisition technology offers a variety of means to inform users about the situation in their homes. However, since only a few sensors are deployed and less data are generated in traditional homes, Wi-Fi and other low-bandwidth methods are often adopted for communication. Thanks to technical advance and rising market demand, sensors are playing a greater role in environmental judgment and system control and have been more widely used in smart homes. The growing number of sensors means a higher demand for data transmission in smart homes when low bandwidth can no longer keep up with future smart homes. 5G technology offers faster transmission and more interfaces that meet the transmission requirements for smart homes to acquire a massive amount of data information. Sensors in high-definition cameras, intelligent door locks, air monitors, facial recognition equipment, etc., are connected to the 5G network through 5G technology, and users can always take a look at their home wherever they are.

(1) *Sensors of various kinds*: Sensors are essentially detection instruments that detect information based on certain rules and output the electrical signal converted from the detected information before transmitting, processing, recording, controlling, storing, or displaying information. There are six major categories of sensors in smart homes (Fig. 1.5): gas sensors, particle sensors, human body induction sensors, security sensors, environmental sensors, and other sensors. These are described as follows:
    (i) *Gas sensor*: A gas sensor converts gas information into corresponding electrical signals. As a part of the fail-safe system, the sensor detects gas leaks or other gas emissions. When connected

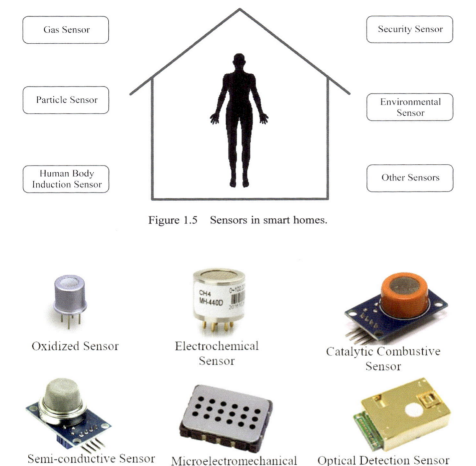

Figure 1.5 Sensors in smart homes.

Figure 1.6 Different types of gas sensors.

to the control system, the gas sensor can automatically ventilate. There are many types of gas detectors, as shown in operating mechanisms, based on different operating mechanisms (Fig. 1.6).

(ii) *Particle sensor*: The particle sensor detects suspended particles in the air. In terms of size, the suspended particles can be divided into fine particles (particle size: 0.1–2.5 μm), medium-sized particles (particle size: 2.5–10 μm) and large-sized particles (particle size: 10–30 μm). Suspended particulate matter may seriously

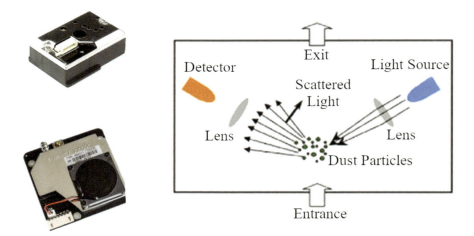

Figure 1.7 Household optical particle sensor.

Figure 1.8 Multiple uses of human body induction sensors.

affect health. Particulate matter with a small diameter can enter the lower respiratory tract. Particulate matter with a diameter of less than 2 μm may go deep into the bronchioles, alveoli, and the bloodstream and diffuse in the blood and blood circulation, resulting in a higher incidence of cardiovascular diseases, respiratory diseases, tumors, etc.

Optical instruments applying the principle of particle light scattering have been used to measure PM2.5. A household optical particle sensor is shown in Fig. 1.7. Such a type of sensor, with smaller size and lower cost, can maintain a relatively high level of linearity and accuracy in particular circumstances.

(iii) *Human body induction sensor*: The human body induction sensor involves a series of technologies used to detect human

Table 1.1 Typical technologies used in human body induction sensors.

Different types of sensors	Induction technologies	Merits
Infrared induction	Infrared sensor acquisition technology and recognition algorithm help to pick out the image suggesting a normal range of human body temperature, determine whether there is someone in the area, and if there is, locate that person.	Protects user privacy
Ultrasonic induction	The ultrasonic positioning technology is used to determine the echo information and thereby locate the person.	Low cost
Image recognition of the body shape	Image sensor acquisition technology and intelligent algorithm help determine whether there is someone in the area, and if there is, locate that person.	Easy to upgrade
Pressure-sensitive induction	The pressure sensor acquisition technology is used to sense the pressure change on the floor and locate the person.	Easy to hide and analyze data
Radio positioning	Similar to ultrasonic induction technology, radio positioning uses radio (radar) detection technology to determine whether there is someone in the area, and if there is, locate that person.	Accurate positioning

existence in a space. The multiple uses of human body induction sensors are shown in Fig. 1.8, and typical technologies used in such sensors are shown in Table 1.1. Checking the status of people in a household is an important aspect for future smart home design, and creating a home environment that can respond to the people living in it is becoming the core of the smart home system. Human body induction sensors are commonly used in emergency rescue and burglary prevention in a house.

(iv) *Security sensor*: Image sensors and cameras are typical security sensor devices. They ensure security by taking photos. As an important component of a digital camera, the image sensor converts optical image information into electronic signals. As technology advances, electronic and digital imaging gradually replaced chemical and analog imaging. Most existing image sensors use semiconductor image sensors, which are divided into charge-coupled device (CCD) sensors and complementary metal oxide semiconductor (CMOS) sensors. Both are based on metal oxide semiconductor (MOS) technology, with MOS capacitors being the basis of CCD sensors and MOS field effect transistors being the basis of CMOS sensors.

(v) *Environmental sensor*: Temperature sensor is a major part of environmental sensor in the home, and a thermistor is widely used in consumer-level commercial temperature sensors.

Thermistor is a type of thermosensitive element made based on a physical characteristic, that is, the electrical resistivity of a metal or semiconductor changes significantly with the temperature. The temperature coefficient of the thermistor can be positive or negative. Different temperature coefficients divide thermistors into positive temperature coefficient (PTC) thermistors, negative temperature coefficient (NTC) thermistors, and critical temperature resistor (CTR). Thermistors are widely used as temperature sensors (NTC thermistors are normally used), self-resetting overcurrent protectors, automatic constant temperature heating elements (PTC thermistors are normally used), and temperature control alarms (CTR thermistors are normally used).

(2) *The application of wireless sensor network in 5G smart home*: In smart home applications, old-fashioned wired sensors have some limitations: the sensors connected to the bus are expensive, substantially driving up the cost of sensor networking; wiring is somewhat difficult in some parts of the house; the protocols of software and hardware on different types of sensors and control system are not compatible. As the wireless sensor network technology keeps developing and maturing, old-fashioned wired sensors were gradually replaced by the more advantageous wireless technology-based sensor products.

Technology keeps moving forward, so does 5G technology. Sensors can thus connect to the Internet more conveniently through 5G, making it easier for users to control their homes.

Most wireless sensor networks consist of sensor nodes, receiver nodes, and management nodes. As the most basic unit in wireless sensor

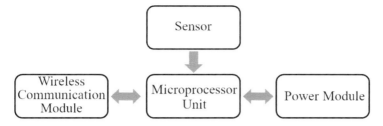

Figure 1.9 The structure of a wireless sensor node.

networks, sensor nodes are distributed in different monitoring areas based on the purpose of measurement. Unified network rules or communication methods are needed for sensor nodes to communicate with other nodes and form a complete and sound wireless sensor network. The structure of a wireless sensor node has four parts, as shown in Fig. 1.9: sensor, microprocessor unit, wireless communication module, and power module.

In tomorrow's smart homes, wireless modules and sensor networks supported by 5G technology will completely change the sensor network; 5G-supported sensor network will be one of the prospective human-centered applications, and its acquisition capabilities will beat that of anything perceivable and deliver a more comfortable, safe, and convenient life experience.

1.2.1.3 *IoT in the 5G era*

(1) *How 5G and IoT are connected*: The wider application of 5G will significantly increase the speed of information transmission in the wide-area network (WAN), yet 5G cannot make devices recognize each other. As a supplement to device recognition technology, IoT technology can make interconnected devices in smart home scenarios a reality and assist 5G in ensuring a smart home at the stub network.

With the development of science and technology, particularly the advancement of the information technology revolution brought about by the Internet, communication between people can happen anytime, anyplace. Some then want the same communication between people and things. The IoT is one such example. It provides a unique identification for people, computers, mechanical equipment, digital equipment, animals, objects, etc., and enables identification and data transmission, wired or wireless, between people and things, and between different things. 5G has expanded, to a large extent, the communication pipeline between the terminal and the Internet, and the number of terminals connected to the Internet saw exponential growth.

In recent years, the concept of "smart home", which is popular both at home and abroad, represents the application of IoT technology in the field of consumer electronics. For example, Google's Google Home, Apple's HomeKit, and Amazon's Echo use smart speakers or mobile phones as the IoT systems and products at the ecological entrance of smart homes; in China, Huawei's HiLink, Haier's U-home, Midea's Meiju, Skyworth's Swaiot, Xiaomi's MIJIA, etc., use their main products as the IoT systems and products at the ecological entrance of smart homes.

These ecological entrances need to be supported by big traffic, low latency, and wide-range connections. These information "pipeline" requirements exactly match the technical characteristics of 5G. A combination of ecological entrance and 5G will create "chemistry", significantly enhancing user experience.

(2) *5G brings about new changes in IoT*: 5G + IoT can be applied in consumer electronics, trade, industry, medical equipment, and other fields. We are most familiar with applications in the field of consumer electronics, such as shared bicycles, smart homes, wearable devices, health and medical equipment, and other devices with remote control features. In particular, in the field of smart homes, more and more traditional home appliances have been connected to the Internet. These "intelligentized" traditional home appliances have become an important part of the smart home, and home appliances are no longer static or passive, like what people used to believe.

These intelligent devices provide a full range of information exchange features to help families maintain efficient and smooth real-time communication with the outside world, which greatly improves the quality of life in an all-round way as people live and work much more efficiently with lower costs. After 2015, the market saw a large number of traditional home appliances with a direct connection to the Internet. The topological structure of these devices in the home networking is shown in Fig. 1.10.

Compared to the traditional network structure of a smart home, the new type of smart home network topology removes the home control center, and the connection with the home gateway serves only as a

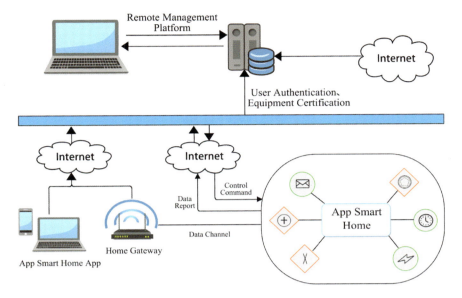

Figure 1.10 New smart home network topology.

data path to access the Internet. The home gateway is merely a channel for data's access to the Internet; it does not analyze or crunch the data. Moreover, all the devices directly exchange data and information with the cloud server. This requires the cloud to have the following features: (1) it should be flexible, expandable, and can support direct access to the cloud server by different types of smart devices or even the same type of smart devices with different features; (2) it should be readable and capable of analyzing and controlling the accessed device data as well as cleaning and processing the collected Big Data by using data tools for the understanding of cloud intelligence.

5G + IoT has huge implications for modern life, while opening up new room for development in the communications, manufacturing, software, and internet industries. That explains why many high-tech companies include "AI + IoT" in their future development. For the communications industry, "smart communities" and "smart cities" will bring substantial demands for device access, placing greater demands for the coverage of communication signals; traditional hardware manufacturers will have to enhance "soft power" to respond to the intelligent demands for devices in various application scenarios; the software industry will have to increase the awareness of hardware and combine connection capabilities of different hardware while providing intelligent solutions to the industry; the IoT can provide stable and reliable Internet service access technologies for massive amounts of devices for the Internet industry. The IoT has pointed to new directions for the development of traditional or high-tech industries. The future of the Internet of Everything starts with connectivity.

(3) *5G shows new ways to upgrade IoT*: For 5G-based smart homes, the stub network still needs to cooperate with the short-distance interconnection communication technology to convert the control signal from the 5G network into an interconnection protocol more suitable for stub network equipment when heading toward the home stretch. Bluetooth, Li-Fi (light fidelity), NFC (near field communication), RFID (Radio Frequency Identification), Wi-Fi, ZigBee, Z-Wave, etc., are common IoT-related short-range (0–100 m) wireless connection protocols.

Low power-consuming interconnection technology in the WAN is applied in scenarios different from that of 5G technology. Long-distance WAN wireless connection technology in the field of smart home cannot be separated from NB-IoT and LoRa. With the formulation of the 5GPPP (a 5G research organization set up by the European Union) standards, NB-IoT also worked out the 5G-NBIoT specifications. The protocol is mainly targeted at WAN devices with strict requirements for power consumption. These devices require low latency and low power consumption instead of big traffic. LoRa emerged earlier than NB-IoT. In August 2013, Semtech rolled out a new type of chip to the industry. The chip is based on the ultra-long range and low power-consuming data transmission technology (LoRa, short for Long Range) below 1 GHz. LoRa mainly operates in free frequency bands (i.e., unlicensed frequency bands) worldwide, including 433 MHz, 868 MHz, and 915 MHz. The LoRa network is mainly composed of four parts: terminal (built-in LoRa module), gateway (or base station), server, and cloud, and its application data enables two-way transmission. NB-IoT uses a cellular frequency spectrum network and optimizes itself for spectrum effectiveness. The license fee for frequency band use is extremely high, and the license is only available for a few operators. As LoRa now uses free frequency bands and open standards, its security has been, to some extent, questioned.

Table 1.2 A comparison of NB-IoT and LoRa's technical indicators.

Technology	NB-IoT	LoRa
Technical features	Cellular	Chirp spread spectrum
Network deployment	Reuse with existing cellular base stations	Independently build the network
Frequency band	Operator's frequency band	150 MHz–1 GHz
Transmission range	Long range	Long range (1–20 km)
Speed (kb/s)	<100	0.3–50
Number of connections	200 k/cell	200–300 k/hub
Terminal battery run time	About 10 years	About 10 years
Cost (dollar/module)	5–10	5

Table 1.2 compares the technical features of these two WAN connection technologies.

5G will bring about new changes to the interconnection technologies at the stub network. First, for terminal devices using short-range wireless protocols, 5G has lower latency, so embedded low-performance processors will encounter a bottleneck: data processing. This requires an upgrade of short-range networking and data transmission protocols. For instance, in recent years, Wi-Fi protocol standards have been fully shifted to Wi-Fi 6 in a bid to avoid data transmission bottlenecks at the stub network. Therefore, 5G also contributed to the upgrading of upstream and downstream hardware companies in the development of short-range wireless IoT technology.

(4) *The combination of 5G and IoT*: In terms of operating systems, different smart devices use different software systems. Different hardware performance and application scenarios adopt a variety of terminal operating systems translated from FreeRTOS, RTLinux, Brillo, LiteOS, OpenWrt, and Android Open-Source Project. Realizing IoT in these terminal operating systems calls for a standard software framework. A platform-based IoT terminal system software framework (Fig. 1.11) should normally include at least the device layer, platform architecture protocol layer, and the application layer.

The device layer has to define abstract hardware interfaces as well as the interfaces across operating systems; the platform architecture protocol layer needs to design software such as protocol standard conversion, device discovery, and cloud data communication; the application layer has to present the application on the smart device's terminal system.

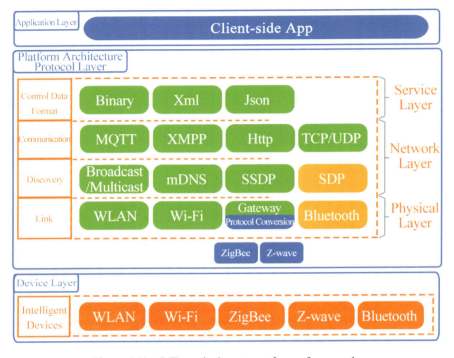

Figure 1.11 IoT terminal system software framework.

An enterprise's cloud platform can be used to serve its own IoT system after it has been built. Furthermore, the enterprise has to extend the features of cloud platforms to enable third-party cloud platform's access for data sharing and win–win cooperation among enterprises.

1.2.2 *The product form of smart home*

1.2.2.1 *Product intelligence: The foundation of everything*

Product intelligence is what underlies the development of the smart home industry. Home automation will lead nowhere without smart products. A good smart product often marks the start of friendly man–machine interaction because in most cases, people's understanding of smart homes starts with a smart product, which shows people's initial feelings and experience of smart homes.

In fact, there is no clear distinction between the definition of smart products and traditional products. The most obvious and intuitive difference lies in the fact that smart products can deliver convenience for users in a particular feature to make users' lives healthier, safer, more convenient, comfortable, and energy-saving with the help of the network, Big Data, IoT, and AI. That is to say, smart products are capable of meeting people's needs.

For example, the smart TV can perform multiple functions after it is connected to the Internet, such as gesture games, live broadcast, channel, program selection and volume adjustment through voice, and project screen interaction with the mobile phone. After the smart refrigerator is connected to the Internet, users can watch videos on TikTok and listen to music on the large screen. The fridge can also offer integrated services covering food purchases, food management, and recipe recommendations through interconnection with the shopping mall.

For washing and drying all-in-one machines and multi-tube washing machines, a fixed-time appointment feature is available on the app. Besides, the washing procedure can match automatically based on clothes' fabrics, colors, etc., best washing time is chosen according to water hardness, and laundry detergent is put in a proper amount based on its concentration; the intelligent air conditioner can automatically read the current environment temperature and adjust the temperature mode; a smart door lock can be opened with fingerprints, passwords, or through facial recognition.

Looking ahead, smart products will achieve leapfrog development. Smart products are predicted to have the following characteristics:

(1) Realize all-round perception based on ubiquitous advanced sensors.
(2) Realize real-time information acquisition and ensure stable equipment services through the in-depth integration of the IoT, cloud platforms, 5G, etc.
(3) The device is able to think like a human through the expansion capabilities of Big Data, AI, and chips.

1.2.2.2 Scene intelligence: The development of IoT

Although smart products often represent people's initial impression of smart homes, the experience one acquired from a smart product tends to be one-sided. The single product is like a scented yet fleetingly falling petal in the air, which can never be compared to the sensory comfort brought about by the fragrance of the entire garden. Therefore, scene intelligence is the best way to attract people to these good products. Basically, through real-life scene design, some smart home-related good smart products are integrated together to deliver a whole set of scene-based services for people to experience firsthand the unique charm of a scene-based smart home.

Compared to 4G, 5G, with lower latency, lower power consumption, and higher bandwidth, offers more real-time, stable, and faster scene-based experience and services. 5G-based home scene design has become one of the most discussed topics. Scene intelligence represents the future of home IoT, and smart home has ushered in a golden age.

With the commercialization of 5G technology, scene intelligence will serve as the catalyst and condiment in our home life. Based on people's preferences and requirements for various scenarios, scene intelligence adopts AI speech and image recognition technology to promptly control the corresponding smart products in the home and create a romantic and beautiful immersive atmosphere for us, making a series of device movements something that happens naturally. Scene intelligence meets home life needs while delivering a fantasy-like experience of seeing "clouds leisurely moving in the sky".

(1) *The initial stage of scene intelligence*: In the early days of its development, scene intelligence was simply divided into two different connotation levels based on the demands and feelings of different groups of people: space scene and time scene. Space scene refers to the placement of smart products in the home based on the spatial location. In a particular space, we can trigger the device according to our own preferences, so that the device can provide us with corresponding services. The time scene is slightly different from the space scene as the devices can be placed anywhere in the space and connect with each other when needed to offer a freer and more convenient scene experience.

Common space scenes in our lives include living room, kitchen, bedroom, elder's room, and children's room. When we are having a break in the living room in the summer heat, we can experience the living room scene (Fig. 1.12). The large-screen OLED TV is playing the most popular programs, the air conditioner's temperature is set at a degree that makes us feel the most comfortable, the light is switched to the most comfortable brightness, the air purifier is racing against

The Past and Present of Smart Home 23

Figure 1.12 Living room scene.

Figure 1.13 Kitchen scene.

the clock to take in harmful substances in the air, and the sweeper is quietly and carefully cleaning every corner of the room.

At this moment, we are hungry and want to cook something in the kitchen. The kitchen scene is ready for you at any time (Fig. 1.13), with the fresh and seasonal vegetables in the refrigerator and the

Figure 1.14   Bedroom scene.

appetizing rice in the rice cooker. Today's list of recommended dishes is displayed on the refrigerator's large screen, and the vegetable washing machine is cleaning the ingredients we have chosen. Meanwhile, we can watch recipes and cooking videos on the large screen of the kitchen ventilator.

We can switch to the bedroom scene (Fig. 1.14) when it's getting late and a rest is needed. The curtains are closed, the bedroom TV is switched to sleep mode, and the main light, ambient light, and OLED reading light are slowly dimmed. In the meantime, the warm light comes out of the night lamp, the temperature is properly adjusted, and the humidifier starts to moisturize the air. It's getting quieter, and we gradually fall asleep.

"Elders are treasures". The care for the elderly in the family cannot be ignored. The elder's room care scene is shown in Fig. 1.15. When the elderly have to rest in the evening, the wallpaper TV enters sleep mode, the bedside smart alarm clock has set the wake-up time, the air purifier is working silently, and the intelligent sensor light belt is

Figure 1.15 The elder's room care scene.

installed under the big comfy bed. When the elders get up at night, the sensor strip will light up for them.

(2) *5G scene intelligence in the 5G era*: Scene intelligence emerged in the market and developed early in the 4G era, yet its advancement has long been limited by the low transmission rate and time delay. Consequently, scene intelligence failed to make it to the households and can only be demonstrated in large exhibition halls and large-scale exhibitions. Compared to 4G, 5G will see a 10-fold increase in its transmission rate and the equipment's response speed. As 5G technology becomes more commercialized, the transmission rate will increase tremendously with a short time delay, suggesting a brighter future for scene intelligence and more possibilities in people's lives.

At the same time, 5G supports the access of more smart devices. Currently, the smart home sample rooms provided by leading home furnishing brands generally support the access and control of up to six to eight smart products. Hopefully, the implementation of 5G technology could make the access of more than 20 smart items to a room with smooth control a reality. 5G technology offers a strong foundation for promoting and popularizing scene intelligence.

The optimization and upgrading of smart device sensor technology and the advent of 5G added a new dimension to scene intelligence, which is divided into passive scene intelligence and active scene intelligence based on the degree of intelligence.

Passive scene intelligence is more commonly seen in today's market. It includes the space scene intelligence and time scene intelligence in the initial stage, as previously mentioned. Moreover, there are more ways for setting and starting the scenes. Passive scene intelligence means we set up smart scenes that fit our own hobbies and habits through mobile phones or other smart terminals and then activate devices in the scene to perform actions accordingly at one moment through voice or gestures. Common passive scene intelligence available today includes going home, leaving home, sleeping, getting up, and entertainment. A number of smart home manufacturers on the market are also rolling out unique passive scene intelligence services.

Compared to the passive type, active scene intelligence is more free, flexible, and considerate. Active scene intelligence automatically models

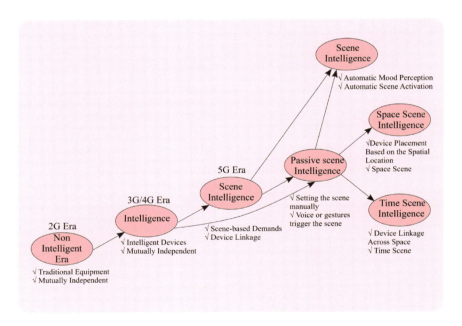

Figure 1.16   The development process of 5G and scene intelligence.

with data generated by various sensors at home and recognizes our daily behaviors such as eating, pooping, sleeping, and playing through the model while constantly optimizing the model during the recognition process so as to realize some highly accurate autonomous perceptions while providing us with a series of scene-based services that needs no setting up or activating. For example, when a couple is arguing at home, active scene intelligence would recognize the scene of quarrel through their postures and tones, the smart speaker will become a gentle mediator, and the smart large-screen TV will turn to a smart photo album, with the family's sweet moments in the past looping continuously on the screen. Besides, the smart tea table will automatically make fragrant green tea to reduce the couple's internal heat, and warm light in the background will help break the ice.

The development process of 5G and scene intelligence is shown in Fig. 1.16. With further promotion and application of 5G technology, scene intelligence will make the interconnection between home products smoother and more convenient. It improves the user experience while breaking the data barriers between different devices, so that user needs can be considered and integrated in an all-round way to get closer to and truly realize the Internet of everything. In this way, smart homes will be available in every household to light up our lives and enable us to embrace a better future.

Chapter 2

The Foundation of the Integration of Smart Home and 5G

2.1 Manufacturing Basis: Great Oaks Grow from Little Acorns

2.1.1 *The current situation of manufacturing of a smart home*

As we all know, for all products to be presented to the public, the basic link of manufacturing is inevitable. Only with the manufacturing basis which matches the development level of a smart home can the smart home meet all imaginations for the future. Otherwise, the realization of a smart home can only be "the flower in the mirror or the moon in the water", which is elusive. The development process of the manufacturing basis of a smart home is an evolving process, as shown in Fig. 2.1. The leap-forward development is its remarkable feature, which in essence echoes the level of the overall scientific and technological development and is also the embodiment of scientific and technological achievements at the manufacturing level. In other words, scientific and technological breakthroughs are the fundamental forces that change the manufacturing basis.

At present, the manufacturing basis of the smart home is in a critical period of the transformation of old and new drivers of growth, facing both new problems and new development opportunities. Industry demand and technological innovation help the development of the global manufacturing industry enter the 4.0 stage. The emergence of the 5G+ industrial Internet accelerates the pace of the development of digital manufacturing, provides technical support for the smart home to advance to high-end

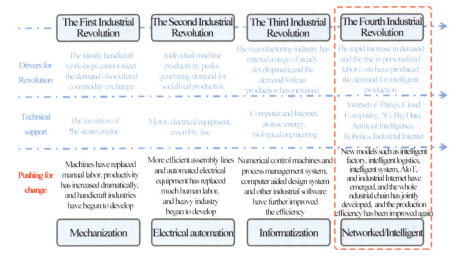

Figure 2.1 Development process of the manufacturing basis of a smart home.

network and intelligence, and brings about a breakthrough change to the manufacturing of a smart home.

2.1.1.1 *Difficulties for the transformation of the manufacturing industry*

In the second decade of the 21st century, the growth rate of the manufacturing industry has slowed down after experiencing rapid development. This is because the current stage of the manufacturing basis cannot meet the diversified market demand and cost reduction demand of the smart home and cannot optimize the manufacturing process. In other words, the current manufacturing basis can no longer meet the needs of the rapid development of a smart home. The manufacturing basis is the foundation of our country and economy. So when we're facing this dilemma, technological transformation is extremely urgent. But the road of transformation is fraught with problems. This is mainly reflected in the following four levels:

(1) Diversification of market demand increases, and personalized customization becomes the new normal of consumption.

(2) With the rapid increase of manufacturing costs, cost reduction and efficiency increase have become the new targets of enterprises.
(3) The data of the production process surge, and network transmission has become a pain point.
(4) Traditional IT architecture cannot meet the needs of informatization of the manufacturing industry, so IT is in urgent need of an upgrade.

2.1.1.2 5G + industrial Internet can break the dilemma

In face of the difficulties in the transformation of manufacturing mentioned above, the state has actively explored the innovation model and policy guidance to promote the industry to "break the difficulties and help the transformation".

At the end of 2017, the State Council passed the *Guiding Opinions of the State Council on Deepening the "Internet plus Advanced Manufacturing" and Developing the Industrial Internet*, which pointed out that by 2025, three to five international industrial Internet platforms should be formed, one million industrial apps should be developed, and one million enterprises should be connected to the cloud.

In June 2018, the Ministry of Industry and Information Technology released The Industrial Internet development action plan (2018–2020) and The 2018 Work Plan of industrial Internet special working group.

On March 17, 2020, State Council Premier Li Keqiang chaired a state council executive meeting, pointing out that support shall be increased for the "Internet Plus" and platform economy. The new forms of digital economy shall be expanded. The traditional industry shall be promoted to speed up the launch on the cloud by relying on the industrial Internet, the life service industry integrating the online and the offline shall be developed, and the development of shared common industrial Internet platforms shall be supported.

On March 20, 2017, the Ministry of Industry and Information Technology issued the *Notice from the General Office of the Ministry of Industry and Information Technology regarding Accelerating the Development of the Industrial Internet*, pointing out that 5G+ industrial Internet should be further implemented, and the momentum of innovation and development should be accelerated and strengthened.

With the in-depth promotion of national policies, 5G can be seen in the application layer, from the network access of manufacturing foundation to the 5G collaboration of intelligent production lines and equipment,

5G conveying robots, 5G visual quality detection, as well as 5G remote video monitoring. and operation and maintenance. In the platform layer, 5G elements are added to the manufacturing level of the industrial Internet in the aspects of edge data collection, system data storage, and establishment and analysis of the industrial mechanism model. The in-depth application of the model of 5G+ industrial Internet at the manufacturing level is changing the production mode of traditional manufacturing. These changes are becoming a cure for the problems in the development of a smart home.

2.1.2 A new manufacturing model for 5G+ industrial Internet

What is the industrial Internet? How is 5G connected to the platform? Let's get to know these key technologies in the new mode of integration of 5G and industrial Internet, and slowly uncover their mysterious veils through layers of explanation like "peeling onions".

2.1.2.1 Technology architecture of the industrial Internet platform

In essence, the industrial Internet platform is an automated assembly line of standardized production and modular packaging of industrial knowledge. It will change the mode of precipitation, dissemination, reuse, and value creation of human knowledge and become the key infrastructure of the new Industrial Revolution, the hub of industrial total factor connection, and the core of industrial resource allocation. The core architecture of the industrial Internet platform (Fig. 2.2) consists of four layers of infrastructure, including the edge layer, infrastructure as a service (IaaS), platform as a service (PaaS), and software as a service (SaaS) and security protection running through all levels. It integrates multiple technologies, such as data acquisition, storage, and computing.

In the final analysis, the industrial Internet platform is still a tool to solve the problem at the manufacturing level. To sum up, the industrial Internet platform = data + computing power + model + application, and its core function is shown in Fig. 2.3.

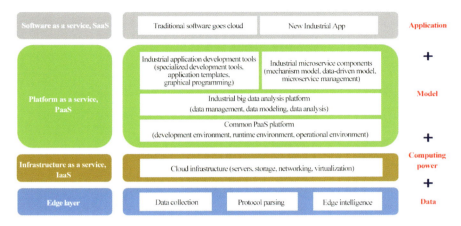

Figure 2.2 Core architecture of the industrial Internet platform.

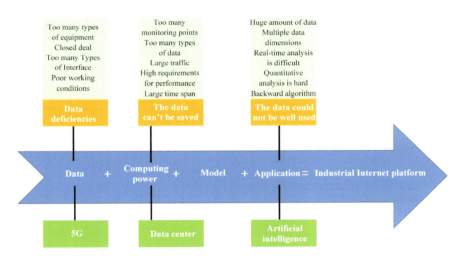

Figure 2.3 Core functions of the industrial Internet platform.

2.1.2.2 *5G access to the industrial Internet platform*

Mobile communication has gone from the 1G era to the 5G era. The introduction of 5G is an effective method to solve the data transmission

34 *The World of 5G: Intelligent Home*

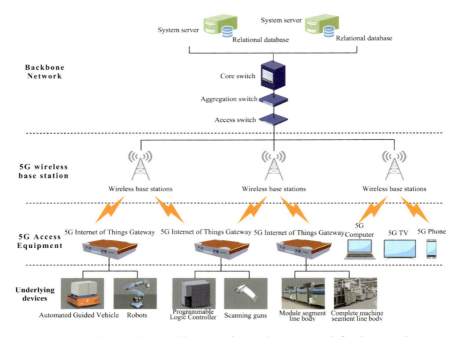

Figure 2.4 5G technology architecture of the industry network for the smart home.

problems faced by each link of smart home manufacturing at present. It is the network foundation of the nation to implement the industrial Internet strategy and an effective means to get through the "initial 1 km" of the industrial Internet.

5G network access is mainly applied to the edge layer of the industrial Internet platform, the main purpose of which is to realize the interconnection and upward transmission of the data of the underlying manufacturing equipment. Figure 2.4 shows the technical architecture of 5G in the industrial network of the smart home.

It can be clearly seen from the above network technology architecture that the manufacturing network after the introduction of 5G is mainly composed of four parts: the underlying equipment, the 5G access equipment, the 5G wireless base station, and the backbone network. These can be described as follows:

(1) *Underlying equipment*: Workshops set 5G customer premise equipment (CPE: 5G CPE is a kind of mobile signal access device that can receive 4G or 5G mobile signals and forward them through Ethernet and wireless Wi-Fi signals). For areas that the factory used to access through Wi-Fi wireless access points, 5G CPE will be adopted to meet the requirement of wireless access to 5G network for devices such as mobile phones, iPads, personal digital assistants (PDAs), automated guided vehicles (AGVs), and printers and to achieve equipment access at the manufacturing level.
(2) *5G access devices*: A large amount of data and time delay requirement, high part of the scene, such as visual inspection robot, the robot or terminals into 5G receiving module, from 5G wireless access instead of cable access, achieve multi-protocol communication equipment, improve the robot or reaction speed and real-time collaborative work efficiency of the equipment.
(3) *5G wireless base station*: A 5G wireless base station to achieve network factory-level coverage.
(4) *Backbone network*: The industrial Internet platform application system where production data enter the backbone network of the park through the 5G wireless base station to realize an intelligent application.

The smart home manufacturing industry has never slowed down in exploring how the 5G technology can be made good use of at the manufacturing level. The 5G technology is introduced into the manufacturing network, which solves the problem of surging data transmission volume in smart factories, realizes the barrage-free communication of the whole manufacturing process elements, and lays a technical foundation for the upward convergence of data at the device layer and system layer.

2.1.3 *The application scene landing under the new mode*

At the level of smart home manufacturing, the new mode of 5G+ industrial Internet mainly centers on the application of "5G+ intelligent production", "5G+ intelligent logistics", "5G+ intelligent safety supervision", and other scenarios. The application scenario takes 5G as the basis for data acquisition and transmission, takes the industrial Internet platform as the core, and provides customized solutions for manufacturing in accordance with the concept of integration and full coverage. Scenes are both integrated and independent of each other.

2.1.3.1 5G + intelligent production

Based on the production, 5G+ intelligence building data-driven "planned production schedule", "manufacturing execution", "quality management", "equipment management", "process management", and other factors of production process control implement a full range of information on production status and visualization, raise the intelligence of the production operation management level, reduce operating costs, and improve production efficiency.

(1) The advanced planning system (APS) is mainly responsible for monthly planning and production scheduling, six-day planning, and distribution of production and operation plans. According to the production line capacity information, material set information, and other resource information, the production planning and scheduling system cooperate with each department and each operation unit to efficiently and orderly arrange production and realize the intelligent scheduling of production operations. The application of the production scheduling system improves the accuracy of the plan and the rate of completion and shortens the delivery cycle.
(2) The manufacturing execution system (MES), the key to achieving each batch product, can not only trace real-time production information collection, information processing materials, quality and production work order, and the order of binding but also realize the procurement of raw materials, the finished product of customer complaint handling, as well as the production process improvement. The manufacturing execution system can also provide enterprises with the functions of plan execution, production efficiency monitoring, key material traceability, whole process quality traceability, comprehensive statistics of statements, visualization of production data, and so on.
(3) The quality management system (QMS), with the production process quality information summary and online quality control as the core and comprehensive quality tracking and management of the raw material and product whole life cycle of enterprise, establishes a rapid

and efficient process for quality feedback, quality process, and quality tracking mechanism, supports the production and operation of the enterprise management, promptly and effectively guarantees the quality of the product.
(4) The equipment management system (EMS), which realizes the digital supervision of equipment in the production process by combining with 5G, collects the key operating parameters and real-time data of each automation control equipment in production through the interface, through the man–machine interface to achieve remote monitoring and operation of the corresponding automation equipment and to achieve the whole line of production equipment and product information collection, status display, alarm and fault processing, trend chart display, report processing, and other functions to help operators or managers quickly diagnose the system fault.
(5) The process management system (PMS), which can realize new product introduction, can process route setting as well as process bill of materials (BOM) management and production technology improvement. The requirements of the production equipment, environment, and production conditions are issued through the process management system to improve the consistency of the production process, and through Big Data mining and analysis, the best process route of similar products is analyzed to comprehensively improve the production efficiency and product quality of products.

2.1.3.2 5G + intelligent logistics

5G+ intelligent logistics, relying on the "5G+ WMS (warehouse management system) + WCS (storage control system) + AGV (automatic guided vehicle)" for the construction of an intelligent three-dimensional warehouse, construction of WMS autonomous trigger logistics demand, WCS autonomous control equipment layer, and AGV autonomous intelligent path planning of intelligent logistics way, improved the production assembly collaborative efficiency as well as reducing cost and increasing efficiency at the same time to promote the establishment of a modern logistics system. Figure 2.5 shows the application diagram of "5G+ intelligent logistics".

The warehouse management system (WMS) provides the distribution of the material demand plan and the function of material inventory

38 The World of 5G: Intelligent Home

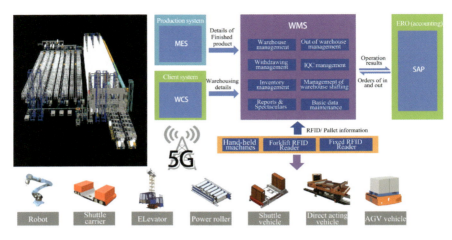

Figure 2.5 Application diagram of "5G Intelligent Logistics".

management for enterprises. The warehouse management system obtains the demand plan of various raw materials in the process of planning and scheduling, and sends the demand plan and dynamic adjustment information to the logistics system promptly and accurately, and guides the logistics system to promptly and accurately feed materials. In the process of production, materials used, through the work order and production batch correlation, trace the production history to achieve material tracking.

The warehouse control system (WCS) mainly uses the task engine and the message engine to optimize and decompose tasks, analyze execution paths, and use a programmable logic controller to control the system to reach the underlying devices under instructions and guide their direction and movement path. The whole system can monitor the material and equipment in real time through the remote visual monitor screen, and analyze and process the data.

2.1.3.3 5G + intelligent safety monitoring

The global security monitoring based on the 5G network layout, which can effectively extend the scope of the layout, implementation enterprise to production safety and life management of "intelligent" regulation, improves enterprise to manufacture the process with no dead Angle monitoring ability and park security patrol, intelligent life in the remote management level, to speed up the enterprise processing and visualization

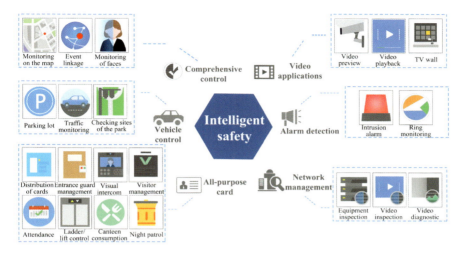

Figure 2.6 Application diagram of "5G+ Intelligent Safety Supervision".

traceability of abnormal situation. Figure 2.6 shows the schematic diagram of the application of "5G+ Intelligent Safety Supervision".

2.2 Network Foundation: Let the Smart Home be Capable of Connecting Everything

2.2.1 *Home network for smart home*

In the current 5G era background, with the increasing number of smart home appliances in the context of smart home, devices have increasingly higher requirements for mobile connections in a progressively rich family scene design, such as home appliances control, face pay, monitoring, security, remote high-definition video, and other life scenes, developing the family bandwidth in the direction of high speed, low latency, and mobility. Home network access will gradually transition to 5G mobile broadband access and gigabit fiber access phase.

2.2.1.1 *5G mobile broadband access*

With the development of mobile communication from 1G to 5G, in the access layer of the communication network, the performance of mobile communication in various aspects such as the upstream and downstream speed, network time delay, and the number of devices accessed has been comparable to that of the fixed network broadband fiber. In the era of 5G smart home, it is possible to enter the home with 5G mobile broadband, which can replace the broadband fiber access of the conventional fixed network and carry out the wireless network coverage of the whole house. 5G mobile broadband provides access to the home through the 5G CPE network, so 5G CPE can be used as a mobile home gateway, providing Wi-Fi access.

From the perspective of domestic market prospects, short-term rentals, small and micro enterprises, shops, rural areas, old communities, and other places where fixed network broadband is not popular, the Internet can be quickly accessed this way. From the perspective of Europe, the United States and other overseas regions, due to high labor costs and complicated ownership of rights of way, property rights, and land rights, the penetration rate of optical fiber in European operators is only about 30%. Mobile broadband penetration has a large market in rural or underdeveloped areas with a low penetration rate of optical fiber overseas. In the future 5G era, as shown in Fig. 2.7, home smart devices such as large-screen intelligent control center, super TV, large-screen refrigerator, and air conditioner are connected to 5G CPE through Wi-Fi, and then CPE is connected to the Internet through the 5G base station, so as to provide mobile broadband access for families and meet the needs of home networking for the smart home.

2.2.1.2 *Home indoor networking needs*

Optical modem + router is the standard configuration of the general home network at present, but in such a network environment, there are often some corners of the network that may be disconnected. So, in view of the future increase in intelligent home appliances for the whole house, how can one ensure that all equipment can be connected to the network at any time anywhere? The smart home scenario has high stable connection requirements for a home network. Therefore, irrespective of whether it is connected to the home through the external optical fiber broadband to the operator or connected to the home through the 5G mobile broadband, indoor networking within the home must be considered.

(1) Home indoor networking needs: As many family devices require a Wi-Fi connection, smart homes need to meet the full coverage of the

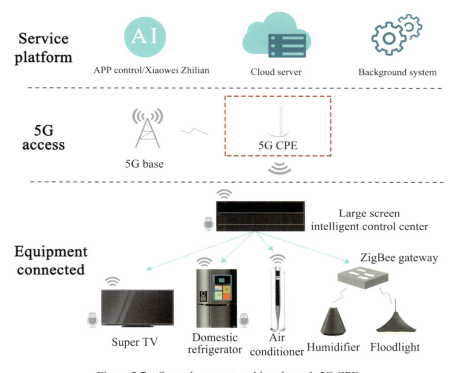

Figure 2.7 Smart home networking through 5G CPE.

family Wi-Fi scheme according to the actual house types to build a high-quality network foundation for the smart home to be built. As shown in Table 2.1, the following requirements should be considered in the construction of the smart home network.

(2) Topology of indoor networking: The smart home scenario requires more and more high indoor networking. As shown in Fig. 2.8, taking external optical fiber access as an example, after the optical fiber is connected to the optical modem, the AC + AP network access mode is formed through access controller (AC) and access point (AP). Among them, the AC connection optical modem needs to have functions of wireless control, routing and switching, and Ethernet power supply; AP is responsible for wireless Wi-Fi access.

In the design of AC + AP topology for a home network, the considerations are shown in Table 2.2. The requirements of wired and wireless

Table 2.1 Requirements for smart home network construction.

Serial number	Requirements
1	Meet the whole house gigabit network. The network cable needs to be at least Category 6 (cat 6) cables
2	Each room should be wired, with at least one Type 86 network panel access point reserved
3	All indoor Type 86 network panel access points are laid to the home information box through network cables
4	The room with the TV needs to have at least two network cables
5	All wired lines must be labeled to facilitate networking between devices and quick positioning in case of problems
6	There should be no dead corner in the Wi-Fi network coverage in the room, and seamless switching between different rooms in the family must be guaranteed

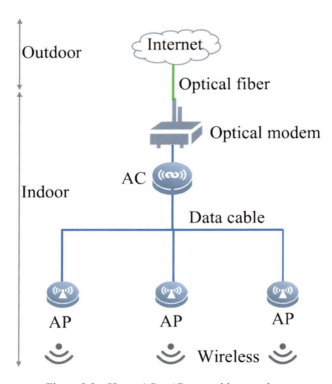

Figure 2.8 Home AC + AP networking topology.

Table 2.2   Matters needing attention in AC + AP topology design of the home network.

Serial number	Matters needing attention
1	The AC is connected directly to the optical modem through the network cable
2	AC to AP is connected by the network cable
3	The size of AP is the same as that of the conventional 86 network panel, and at least one network cable port should be reserved on the AP panel, so that devices can also access the network through the wired way
4	As an access point of wireless network, AP can carry out Wi-Fi wireless expansion to meet the Wi-Fi coverage of the whole house
5	The terminal can be connected to the AP wirelessly and then connected to the network

(Wi-Fi) connections should be combined to meet the coverage of the home network.

2.2.2 Smart home gateway in the 5G era

The smart home gateway is the network equipment inside a modern family. Its role is to help home users connect to the Internet, including the Internet connection of all kinds of intelligent devices located in the family, and to make these intelligent devices communicate with each other. From the technical point of view, the home gateway in the home and from the inside to the outside achieves bridging, routing, protocol translation, address management, and transformation functions, assumes the responsibility of the firewall, and provides IP voice telephony and other services. At present, the main way for the smart home gateway to access the Internet is optical fiber access, but in fact, the laying of optical fiber cannot be implemented in many complex terrains and sparsely populated areas in the world, and the coverage rate of optical fiber in the world is not high. The birth of 5G undoubtedly provides a solution for the comprehensive popularization of smart home gateways. 5G has a high bandwidth comparable to optical fiber, and 5G access does not need complex ground lines, so it is easy to be promoted. It can be expected that the smart home gateway based on 5G broadband access will provide a powerful driving force for the development of the smart home.

2.2.2.1 *The birth process of the smart home gateway*

The smart home gateway is born with the rapid development of the Internet and the increasing number of intelligent home terminals. With the rapid development of the global Internet, including mobile phones, a variety of home intelligent terminals emerge in an endless stream and all household appliances are moving toward the direction of intelligence. At the same time, all kinds of broadband technologies continue to appear, especially the rapid advancement of fiber to the home (FTTH), and the network bandwidth of home users is gradually moving toward 100 MB, even 1 GB and 10 GB, thus giving birth to the smart home gateway. The emergence of the smart home gateway provides strong network support for the smart home. The development of the smart home gateway has gone through exploratory, formation, and intelligent stages, as shown in Fig. 2.9.

In recent years, the IoT has seen explosive development, leading to the rapid development of the smart home. A variety of home devices have begun to connect to the Internet and have intelligent functions. In order to meet the requirements of the network connection of the intelligent home, all major operators have launched the smart home gateway. Compared to the Home Gateway Unit (HGU), the smart home gateway needs to be significantly upgraded in terms of hardware configuration, and the software also needs to have more complex functions. For example, the software needs to communicate with many background servers, and the software needs to support the remote installation of various software and plug-ins to achieve a variety of intelligent functions. At the same time, with the vigorous development of 5G, the smart home gateway with 5G

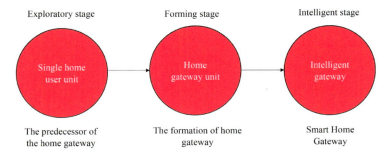

Figure 2.9   The development stages of the smart home gateway.

as the bearer network will also show vigorous development. The smart home gateway can support more electronic devices within the family to form a family local area network (LAN). In particular, the smart home gateway has powerful backstage server support, so that all kinds of devices within the family can achieve mutual communication. The appearance of a typical smart home gateway backplane is shown in Fig. 2.10.

Various terminals in the home network can communicate with the smart home gateway through the user side interface of the smart home gateway. The smart home gateway forwards, controls, and manages the data and applications passed through it and interacts with the business platform, smart home platform, and set-top box terminal management platform through the network interface such as optical fiber or 5G, so as to realize the communication between home network and external network, and provide a variety of manageable and controllable applications.

2.2.2.2 Application scenario of the smart home gateway

As the core equipment of the smart home networking, the smart home gateway supports all the networkable devices at home to connect to the home LAN. For home devices supporting wired and wireless networks, the smart home gateway can be connected via wired and wireless networks, respectively. However, some low-power products cannot be connected to the power supply and so batteries need to be installed, such as smart door locks, then how to access the smart home gateway? At present, this kind of product generally accesses the smart home gateway through the way of sub-gateway. The sub-gateway is actually a protocol converter. The sub-gateway connects to the smart home gateway via Wi-Fi and then converts the signal of the smart home gateway to Bluetooth or Zigbee (Zigbee is a kind of bidirectional wireless network technology with low

Figure 2.10 Typical backboard appearance of the smart home gateway.

speed, which is developed according to the IEEE 802.15.4 wireless standard. It has the advantages of low complexity, short distance, low cost, and low power consumption).

Typical application scenarios of the smart home gateway mainly include home entertainment, home security, and home control. These are described as follows:

(1) Home entertainment: Home entertainment based on the smart home gateway is the most common application scenario of the smart home gateway. Various audio-video terminals in the home are interconnected through the smart home gateway to achieve perfect audio–visual functions.

As shown in Fig. 2.11, computers, set-top boxes, smart TVs, network hard disks, and other devices are connected to the smart home gateway through a wired network, while mobile phones, tablet computers, smart speakers, and other devices are connected to the smart home gateway through a wireless network, and USB hard disks are connected to the smart home gateway through a USB interface. Based on the smart home gateway, a LAN within the home is formed.

(2) Home security: Home security based on the smart home gateway is another application scenario of the smart home gateway. For details, refer to the third chapter of the book "The integration of 5G and home security".

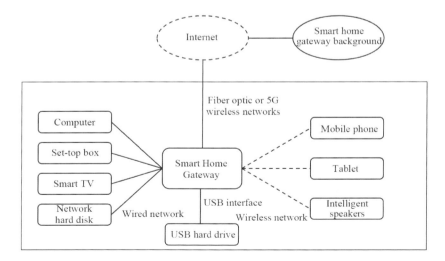

Figure 2.11   A schematic diagram of home entertainment networking.

(3) Home control: Home control based on the smart home gateway is becoming more and more popular. At present, the Wi-Fi connection to the Internet of more and more household appliances such as washing machines, refrigerators, air conditioners, rice cookers, water purifiers, and curtains is supported. Now even sockets and light bulbs also support Wi-Fi connectivity.

As shown in Fig. 2.12, sockets and light bulb devices that do not support Wi-Fi connectivity but support Zigbee connectivity can be connected to the smart home gateway through a sub-gateway.

2.3 System Foundation: A Unified Platform Based on 5G + Four System Technologies

5G, AI, Big Data, the IoT, and cloud computing are all closely related to each other. Big Data is the cornerstone of AI. In fact, neural network algorithms, which have developed rapidly in the field of AI in recent

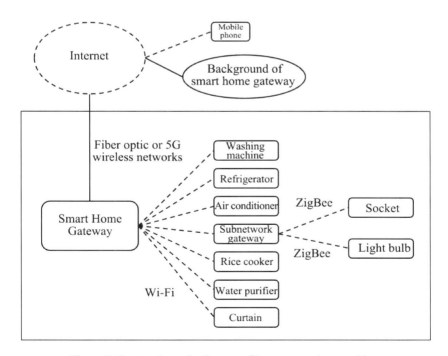

Figure 2.12 A schematic diagram of home control networking.

years, cannot be done without massive data. The IoT without AI will, at best, solve the problem of connectivity rather than bring about a more profound change. For AI algorithms to become more accurate, the data provided by the IoT is important. Cloud computing is the booster of these technologies, which turns traditional IT work into cloud computing based on the network. As a highway of information transmission, 5G provides a strong public infrastructure for the implementation of these technologies. AI, Big Data, the IoT, and cloud computing are dependent on each other and help each other. With the help of 5G, they can provide all walks of life with more rapid image recognition technology, voice recognition technology, natural language understanding technology, user portrait technology, and other latest scientific and technological tools.

2.3.1 *System architecture*

The unified platform based on 5G+ four system technologies can be divided into "horizontal" and "vertical" technology systems. The "horizontal" refers to the system technology involved in the platform, while the "vertical" can be simply divided into hardware and software, as shown in Table 2.3. It can be seen that there are many choices of IoT products or technologies, cloud computing technologies, AI technologies, and Big Data technologies. These technologies will see brand new development and progress in the 5G era. From the technical point of view, the construction of such a complex system as well as the enterprise's hardware capability and software capability has put forward very high requirements, and the investment in research and development is also very huge. It can be said that in the field of electronic information, the enterprise that is capable of building basic system platforms for the IoT, cloud computing, AI, and Big Data in the 5G era will have a longer future.

2.3.2 *Design of a terminal operating system*

Any advance in information science and technology needs a terminal as a carrier. Hardware is an integral part of a unified platform. In the face of intelligent change today, many hardware will be redefined.

Table 2.3 Technical coverage of a unified platform.

Project	Internet of Things	Cloud computing	Artificial intelligence (AI)	Big data
Hardware	Multimedia products, white household appliances, lighting electrical products, wearable equipment, gateway equipment, etc.	Infrastructure as a Service (IaaS), Platform as a Service (PaaS), Software as a Service (SaaS)	Display computing units, tensor computing units, depth computing units, distributed computing facilities, etc.	Data collection, data cleaning, data storage, data calculation, etc.
Software	MCU interrupt software system, embedded real-time software system, modern software operating system, custom software operating system, etc.		TensorFlow tools, Caffe tools, Microsoft Cognitive tools, Torch tools, etc.	

Table 2.4 Classification of intelligent devices.

Classification	Characteristics
Class A	Can run embedded smart devices such as 51 MCU. With hardware control ability, the communication with the modules connected to the Internet adopts serial port, GPIO (General Purpose Input/Output), USB bus, and other common hardware protocols. This kind of product is usually combined with the hardware module of Class B and Class C to form a new intelligent hardware form
Class B	Hardware capable of running real-time operating systems such as Arm Mbed OS, FreeRTOS, and LiteOS. It has high requirements for real-time performance and power consumption
Class C	Able to run modern operating system devices such as Android and Linux that require large amounts of memory

According to the current situation of the smart home, modern smart devices can be divided into several categories, as shown in Table 2.4.

For Class A products, common products include household appliances, lighting desk lamps, etc. At this time, additional hardware modules capable of networking are needed to assist in establishing a unified system platform.

For Class B products, common products include Zigbee gateway, visual doorbell, low-power mobile camera and so on. These products have certain computing power, but they are not capable of running AI algorithms on the end. Instead, they can only present intelligent results by transferring the data perceived by the device to cloud computing through the Internet.

Class C products commonly include mobile phones, TV, tablet computers, super gateways, and so on. Presumably, in the 2020s, these products will have higher performance hardware and may be integrated with a Neural Network Processing Unit (NPU) or a Tensor Processing Unit (TPU), with some common neural network models able to run directly on the hardware.

After determining the hardware scheme of the product and porting the existing software operating system, it is necessary to design the message mechanism to communicate with the unified cloud platform on the basis of the embedded operating system. Let's look at the underlying software architecture of a common IoT operating system (Fig. 2.13).

The Foundation of the Integration of Smart Home and 5G   51

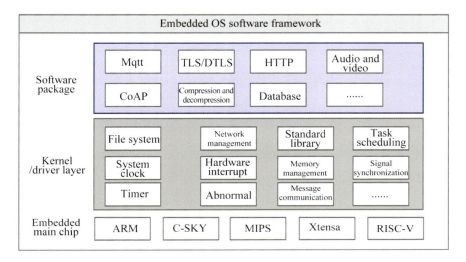

Figure 2.13   Embedded OS software framework.

With a unified software system foundation, an ecosystem of embedded application development is preliminarily provided. The system software package is used to develop and run the secure communication message middleware on the embedded system, and the SaaS interface of the unified platform is called to realize the effect of long connection, and the firmware upgrade and hardware status report are completed.

Regardless of the hardware design and software system used in these smart devices, once the 5G signal is completed in the home, it can reduce the delay between the device and the cloud on the device control link, greatly improving the hardware control experience.

2.3.3 *Design of equipment access network system*

The design of the device access system is shown in Fig. 2.14. At the end of the network covered by 5G, many powerful cloud platforms will provide standardized Software Development Kits (SDKs) for various mainstream embedded operating systems. Most of these embedded systems support common access protocol standards such as MQTT (Message queuing Telemetry Transport) or COAP (Constrained Application Protocol). On the other side of the 5G pipeline, the cloud platform can be said to be the first threshold for IoT devices to access the

52 *The World of 5G: Intelligent Home*

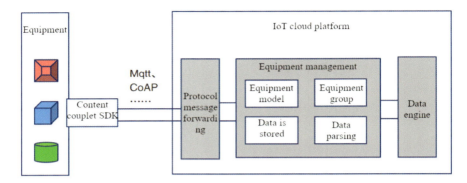

Figure 2.14 Design of the device access system.

Internet. It needs to face a lot of problems, such as the stability and security of the connection of smart devices, the report of rapid state change data of sensing devices and high concurrency, and so on, all of which have become issues to be considered by the cloud platform.

The IoT platform provides the IoT SDK. After the devices are integrated with the IoT SDK, they can safely access the cloud platform of the IoT and use functions such as data storage and data parsing. As the platform is built on the basis of the Internet, 5G is important as a conduit into the cloud. Under the existing mobile network conditions, when the same environment contains high-traffic video devices, the devices at the end of the network are often unable to obtain enough up–down bandwidth, and the stability of the device and the cloud platform is no longer reliable. With the arrival of 5G, the upstream and downstream bandwidth is enough to meet the network requirements of the interconnected devices at the end of the network.

2.3.4 *Design of data system*

Big Data is a brand-new technical framework to extract value from large-volume data through acquisition, storage, and analysis. In some Big Data scenarios that require real-time computation and feedback results, the advantages of 5G pipelines can be effectively exploited.

The data system of the IoT platform acquires a large amount of hardware data, which has a simple structure and high repeatability, and is very easy to be extracted, stored, and cleaned. What value can these data bring

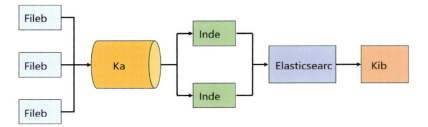

Figure 2.15 Big Data log system.

to the user of the smart home in the end? When deciding on the landing of data, we should think deeply about this. The Big Data industry has dedicated data analysts, and a good data analyst will find something unusual in a pile of seemingly boring data or something that no one else has thought of. In the process of data mining, some of the techniques of AI can be used to help data analysts provide predictions and make decisions based on currently available data. Finally, these predictive models and decisions are output to the visual interface or application processing logic.

One of the simplest Big Data technology scenarios to apply is the landing of device logs. If you want to find the device usage behavior of a certain user at a certain moment, how to quickly locate and find results from the massive device logs? Using the existing open-source software, you can configure the Filebeat log collection tool in the server cluster of the data engine and input the log messages collected by Filebeat into the distributed Kafka message queue. This process realizes the peak clipping of the log collection. Then, the distributed configuration of Elasticsearch is used to achieve the landing of the log search engine. The end user can quickly search the logs using a RESTful interface or view them directly in the Kibana (visual platform) interface, as shown in Fig. 2.15.

2.3.5 *Design of the artificial intelligence algorithm system*

The AI framework almost provides all the cloud distributed deployment scheme and the commercially successful optical character recognition (OCR), facial recognition, speech recognition all shift the AI technology to the cloud from the terminal to AI algorithm under the new era, and the result is the emergence of higher requirements for pipe network. This is an important reason for the era to call for 5G.

AI technology has a rich technical connotation. When designing a unified platform, we should first understand the connotation of AI, so as to realize the effective application of AI technology at the business level with a clear target. After the popularization of 5G, the application scenarios that AI technology can cover will be more extensive. For example, face recognition is an application technology. If the face recognition model is run on the terminal hardware with TPU/CPU, it can only recognize the number of faces in a limited range due to the memory and performance of the terminal. However, if the images sensed by the terminal camera are quickly uploaded to the cloud server through the 5G channel, the face base library that can be recognized will become very large. The recognition results will be transmitted back to the application provider through the 5G channel, which will be able to meet a variety of high requirements of the use scenarios.

2.4 Business Model Basis: New Home Furnishing Business Form in the 5G Environment

2.4.1 *5G+ smart real estate*

Traditional commercial real estate is often operated in relatively simple ways, such as selling houses and decorating houses. With the development of technology and the popularization of 5G technology, commercial real estate is now developing in the direction of intellectualization and the integration of families, communities, and streets. With the popularization of 5G technology, family-centered smart homes can connect and share information with communities centered on convenience services and streets centered on public services through 5G technology, which greatly facilitates residents' lives. Through the 5G technology, users can communicate with the convenience stores and properties in the community at home and communicate with the schools, educational institutions, and supermarkets in the street, which truly and conveniently realizes the application of a modern smart home. With the development of 5G technology, families, communities, and streets are connected into an effective whole, achieving interaction and promoting real estate developers to create modern commercial real estate integrated with 5G technology.

Intelligentization will permeate every link of life, community, and city in the near future, thus inspiring the investment of upstream and downstream industries of the whole real estate industry, promoting the technology transformation and upgrade of architectural design, sensor system, intelligent electrical connectivity, the Internet technology, 5G technology, IoT technology, software platform, cloud, and computing, so as to continue to explore research and development for the real arrival of "5G+ smart real estate".

2.4.1.1 The integration of smart homes and a new generation of commercial real estate

Over the past few years, the real estate industry has been affected by smart home technology. Smart home technology has had a huge impact on the real estate industry, and all indications are that it will continue to have a huge impact, with 81% of home buyers buying a home because they already have a smart home product installed.

With the development of science and technology and the country's efforts to promote the construction of smart cities, the gradual acceleration of urbanization, and the popularization of emerging technologies such as AI technology, IoT, and mobile Internet, the combination of smart home and real estate industry is an inevitable development direction and trend. Smart real estate will provide new ways and development space for the transformation of the real estate industry. However, although the smart home has been around for about 10 years, related technologies and solutions are still emerging. With the support of 5G, Artificial Intelligence Internet of Things (AIoT), and other new technologies, the smart home now has its own innovative features in overall market positioning, overall channel construction, and overall business model construction.

Market division of smart real estate includes smart homes for family residences, villas and mansions oriented to the consumer level, and smart homes for hotel, offices oriented to the office level (enterprises or specific user groups).

(1) Consumption-oriented smart real estate: Smart home scenes and systems for consumer-oriented smart real estate, as shown in Fig. 2.16, are divided according to the scene modes required by users. Common scenes include going home scene, receiving visitor's scene, romantic

Figure 2.16 Smart home scenes and systems for smart real estate at the consumer level.

scene, entertainment scene, reading scene, sleeping scene, getting up scene, leaving home scene, etc. According to the control system, it can be divided into the central control system, environment control system, lighting control system, security monitoring system, background music control system, curtain control system, private theater systems, video intercom system, etc. Each subsystem, respectively, intelligently controls the relevant part of the whole house and works with each other to build the future smart home through the central brain, cloud technology, and 5G technology, so as to realize the smart real estate at the consumer level.

(2) Office-oriented smart real estate: Office-oriented smart real estate is often dominated by public places, as shown in Fig. 2.17, including smart classrooms, smart supermarkets, smart communities, smart parking lots, smart warehouses, smart factories, smart conference rooms, and other application scenarios.

Smart home systems for office-level smart real estate are usually project-based. Large projects often need system-level data connections with various management systems. Under the support of 5G technology, we can use the new generation of information technologies such as mobile Internet, IoT, cloud computing, Big Data, and AI to integrate all kinds of existing resources in the scene, form an information-based and intelligent management mode, and provide convenient services or a safe production environment for enterprises or specific user groups.

The Foundation of the Integration of Smart Home and 5G   57

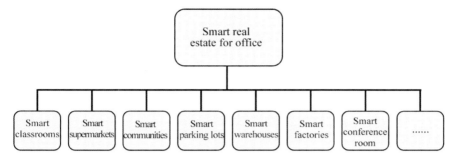

Figure 2.17   Smart home scenes and systems for smart real estate at the office level.

2.4.1.2 *The development prospect of smart real estate*

In the future, with the development and promotion of 5G technology, the development direction of smart real estate projects will provide more equipment space entrance for the smart home. At the same time, with the upgrade of intelligent home appliances, network communication technology, as well as the collaborative innovation and integration development of intelligent software and hardware vendors, a variety of new technologies will work together to create the core value of the smart home in the hearts of users and provide personalized and optional overall solutions for the consumer- and office-level projects. Smart real estate can not only realize the overall home intelligence through 5G technology, Internet technology, AI technology, and smart home appliance technology but also create a smart ecosystem through access to smart property, business circle information, smart medical care, smart government affairs, smart security, smart shopping, and other system functions.

For ordinary families, typical application cases of smart communities supported by 5G technology are shown in Fig. 2.18. As the main living place of the user, the home is at the center of the user's life. With the family as the center, the surrounding area of 300 m is the second level of the user's daily life. At this level, users can experience more convenient community services through 5G technology, including electronic payment, door-to-door maintenance, intelligent access control, and patrol and inspection. In a larger scope, family-centered, and broad community of around 300–3000 m, 5G technology will provide more community life services, including fire protection and sanitation, education, schools,

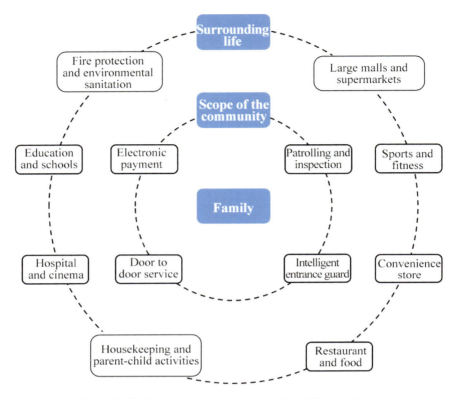

Figure 2.18 Smart community supported by 5G technology.

hospitals and cinemas, family service, catering, convenience stores, sports and fitness, large supermarkets, etc. The widespread popularization of 5G technology will greatly facilitate people's community life.

2.4.2 *5G+ smart new retail*

With the popularization of digital technology and the upgrading of consumer demand, retail also begins to develop in the direction of intelligence. Smart retail refers to the use of the Internet, the IoT, Big Data, AI, and other technologies to optimize the relationship between products, users, and payment to give customers a faster, better, and more convenient shopping experience. In the 4G era, we have enjoyed the sharing economy and mobile payments. In the 5G era, we will live in a world where everything is connected. The new retail scene in the 5G era is not only the connection between people and things but also the connection between things and things, people and things. And it reconstructs the connection network between people and people, people and goods, goods and goods. Although 5G itself is just a kind of technology, it can drive the whole new retail ecosystem and the technology associated with 5G to develop in a transformative way, bringing about all-round changes in social production and life. First, it can subvert the value system. Second, it can improve production efficiency. Third, it can promote technological innovation. Due to the high speed, wide connection, and high reliability of the 5G network, the integration of online and offline communication driven by technology and data has brought new opportunities to retail.

So, what will the new retail look like? The Alibaba group believes the core meaning is that, based on the Internet, enterprises transform and upgrade the production, circulation, and sales process of commodities by using Big Data, AI, and other advanced technological means, thus reshaping the business structure and ecosystem and deeply integrating online services, offline experience, and modern logistics into a new retail model. Zhang Jindong, Chairman of the Suning Group, put forward the concept of "smart retail" at the Two Sessions in 2018. In the future, retail will be smart retail. Smart retail will use the Internet and IoT technologies to perceive consumption habits, predict consumption trends, guide production and manufacturing, and provide consumers with diversified and personalized products and services. There are many different interpretations of a retail phenomenon. In fact, every enterprise has its own views on retail. Different interpretations of enterprises may be from another dimension to think about retail. But no matter how retail changes, the user experience is still the core of retail.

From the interpretation of Alibaba and Suning on new retail or smart retail, we can see the evolutionary history of retail. Both new retail and smart retail use the Internet, Big Data, and other technologies to perceive users' consumption habits, so as to provide consumers with diversified and personalized products and services.

2.4.2.1 *New retail demand in the 5G era*

Consumer products have a life cycle, so how can one connect with consumers during the life cycle of the product? Launching smart new retail and establishing high-frequency connections with consumers is critical to creating a product ecosystem. In fact, the essence of new retail is still retail, which makes users become the core with the help of the Internet, while the essence of traditional retail is the medium of commodity exchange.

In the context of smart new retail, "human" has become the core element of retail activities. Through Big Data, AI, and other technical means, the online and offline scenes can be integrated. So why are we doing new retail? The following factors are the reasons:

(1) Online retail hits the "ceiling".
(2) New technologies such as mobile payment promote the popularity of intelligent terminals in offline scenes.
(3) The rise of a new middle class.

2.4.2.2 5G enables the advantage of new retail

Through the precise selection of product mix, smart new retail creates a deeply rooted scene experience, so as to improve the retail floor efficiency ratio and optimize the cost. Smart new retail uses the thinking of focusing on users to design products, the thinking of experiencing life to construct scenes, and the thinking of conveying value to perform operations. With the power of Big Data, AI technology, and 5G technology, products and stores will be customized and reformed to provide a better consumption experience for customers and achieve cost reduction and efficiency increase for stores. In the future, the retail model will be a new retail model combining the online and offline scenes. The combination of the online and offline scenes does not mean that brick-and-mortar stores open online stores or expand online stores to brick-and-mortar stores, but instead points to the combination of online core advantages and offline core advantages.

The core advantage of the online scene is convenience. We do not have to go out. The core advantage of the offline scene is the customer experience. The new retail of the future, then, will be a combination of these two. How can we see and feel if the product we want to buy is what we want without leaving our house? A feeling comes from many aspects, including hearing, sight, touch, taste, etc. At present, we have the ability to present hearing and sight in front of us through data transformation.

Future science, with the help of AI and 5G technology, will surely bring touch and taste to us through data conversion.

The 5G era will undoubtedly bring us closer to products and let us feel what we want at home. Based on the powerful logistics system of the future, we can also have the physical shopping experience at home.

Chapter 3

Typical Applications of Smart Home–5G Integration

3.1 5G+ Ultra-high Definition (UHD) Television

3.1.1 *Development trend of flat-panel TV*

As its name suggests, flat-panel TVs are TVs with flat screens, as opposed to the traditional CRT TVs. Flat-panel TVs mainly include LCD TVs, plasma display panels, OLED TVs, and other technical types of TV products. Image display with higher definition and true-to-life color, diverse applications, and interaction that delivers excellent experience are what flat-panel TVs aim to realize in the future. In the era of flat-panel TVs, multimedia TVs, digital all-in-one TVs, full HD TVs, 3D TVs, Internet TVs, cloud TVs, smart TVs, 4K UHD TVs, high dynamic range imaging (HDR) UHD TVs, AI voice TVs, and other new forms of TVs have been mushrooming and updating rapidly. In the evolution of flat-panel TV products, display technology and intelligent technology are the main technical focuses (Fig. 3.1).

3.1.1.1 *The convergence trend of TV display and 5G*

The development of flat-panel TV display technology features the increase in display resolution.

With its clear, detailed images and true-to-life, vivid colors, 4K UHD TVs contributed to the prosperity and development of the flat-panel TV industry. However, the market demand for larger-sized flat-panel TVs

64 *The World of 5G: Intelligent Home*

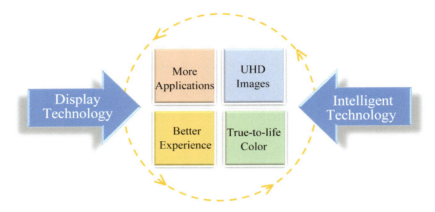

Figure 3.1 The development trend and technical focus of flat-panel TV.

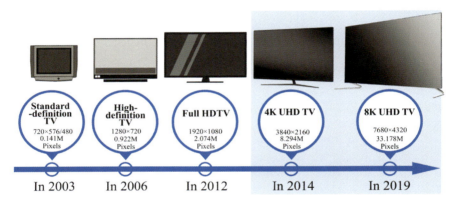

Figure 3.2 The evolution of flat-panel TV display resolution.

continues to grow. Larger size calls for higher resolution as well as clearer, more detailed, and more true-to-life display. Therefore, the 8K UHD TVs with a display resolution of 7680 × 4320 pixels were introduced. Figure 3.2 shows the evolution of flat-panel TV display resolution.

The 8K UHD TV display has 33.178 megapixels, with larger color depth and wider color gamut. The entry-level 8K video with a frame rate of 30 f/s has an uncompressed bitrate of 30 Gb/s; the ultimate 8K video with a frame rate of 120 f/s has an uncompressed bitrate of 144 Gb/s.

The transmission bitrate of entry-level 8K video hit more than 100 Mb/s, which requires extremely strong network transmission capabilities.

At present, the transmission capacity of the digital broadcasting and TV program transmission network does not exceed 40 Mb/s; the maximum rate of 4G is about 100 Mb/s, and the normal rate is roughly 20 Mb/s; the cable network bandwidth can reach 100 Mb/s, yet the effective bandwidth for normal use is only 20 Mb/s. It is apparent that the existing digital broadcasting and TV program transmission networks, 4G networks, and cable broadband networks cannot support 8K video transmission.

5G wireless transmission will be an effective solution for 8K video transmission, and it would be absolutely necessary to integrate 5G into 8K UHD TV products.

3.1.1.2 *The convergence trend of TV intelligence and 5G*

AIoT TV has an excellent interactive experience and the devices are interconnected, making people's lives more convenient. With increasingly diversified AIoT devices and application scenarios, the number of interconnected devices will explode, which inevitably requires more powerful intelligent interaction and device interconnection capabilities from AIoT TVs. However, the current Wi-Fi, 4G, and other network interaction could delay up to 100 milliseconds, and the number of IoT devices that can be accessed is limited, undermining the expansion capabilities of AIoT TVs. 5G can support the interconnection of large-scale smart devices on a small scale and realize the interconnection of a huge number of AIoT devices; meanwhile, 5G's low latency will reduce the interaction latency of AIoT devices to only about 10 ms, which is much faster than the speed of human response and brings about excellent AIoT user experience. It is vital to integrate intelligence with 5G and build family AIoT ecology with 5G smart TV as the center.

3.1.2 *Implementation plan of 5G + 8K smart TV*

3.1.2.1 *5G + 8K smart TV products*

5G + 8K smart TV integrates 5G features with 8K UHD TV. It has a peak bandwidth of more than 1 Gb/s or even 10 Gb/s, supports super-fast download of 8K videos, and can download a 150 GB 8K movie within only 60 s; it supports the access to a massive number of IoT devices, with

66 *The World of 5G: Intelligent Home*

Figure 3.3   5G + 8K smart TV products.

up to 10,000 IoT connected devices per square meter. It also realizes ultra-low interaction latency, merely 10 ms or even 1 ms for IoT devices, delivering an excellent experience for users.

5G + 8K smart TV products (Fig. 3.3) support the access of 5G communication network, and the decoding and display of 5G signal; 8K video programs through 5G; 8K × 4K video decoding and display with a 7680 × 4320 display pixel resolution; AI speech interaction and image interaction; access to a large number of IoT devices and AIoT interconnection.

3.1.2.2 *5G + 8K smart TV system framework*

The 5G + 8K smart TV system framework is shown in Fig. 3.4. The framework is composed of built-in 5G antenna, built-in 5G module, TV module, FRC (frame rate conversion) module, 8K display, camera and MIC (microphone) module, built-in Wi-Fi and Bluetooth modules, etc. In addition to the transmission of video (or image), information between modules, communication through control, status, data, and control buses are also needed for video source identification and AIoT control.

5G + 8K smart TV-related modules and functional requirements are shown in Table 3.1.

3.1.2.3 *Key technologies of 5G + 8K smart TV application*

After the 5G + 8K smart TV system framework is established, some key technologies are needed to make good products for the applications of 5G + 8K smart TV. What are these key technologies then?

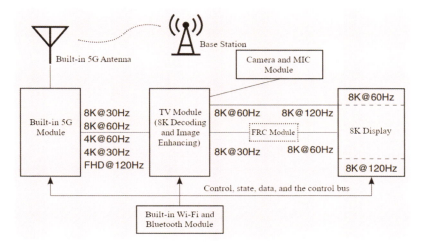

Figure 3.4   5G + 8K smart TV system framework.

First, 5G network access and modulation and demodulation (modem) technologies are needed. These include 5G NR (new radio) carrier aggregation technology, scalable orthogonal frequency division multiplexing (OFDM) subcarrier spacing technology, multiple-input multiple-output (MIMO) multi-antenna signal enhancement technology, bandwidth part (BWP) technology, and uplink and downlink decoupling technology.

Additionally, smart AP technologies and applications based on 5G + 8K smart TVs are required. 5G + 8K smart TV integrates Wi-Fi and Bluetooth modules and switches between 5G signals and Wi-Fi signals through the decoding module. With 5G + 8K smart TV as the AP hotspot, the establishment of a wireless Wi-Fi smart local area network through the Internet is unnecessary for wireless transmission and application of audio and video signals as well as AIoT interconnection and intelligent interaction.

Finally, AIoT technology based on voice and image interaction is needed. With 5G + 8K smart TV terminal as the control center and entrance of smart home, the integration and control of AIoT devices such as household smart electronic equipment and audio and video playback devices enable the interconnection between different smart devices through 5G wireless communication as well as AIoT device control and

68 *The World of 5G: Intelligent Home*

Table 3.1 5G + 8K smart TV-related modules and functional requirements.

Order	Module	Functional requirements
1	Built-in 5G antenna	Receive wireless signals of all 5G frequency bands transmitted by the base station or send the 5G frequency band signals modulated by the built-in 5G module to the base station.
2	Built-in 5G module	Baseband audio and video signals are obtained after demodulation of the signals in the frequency band received by the built-in 5G antenna, and then the baseband audio and video signals are parsed. After that, the signals are transmitted to the TV modules through the high-speed transmission interface. The transmitted signals mainly include video images with a resolution of 8K@30/60 Hz, 4K@30/60 Hz, FHD@120 Hz, etc., and audio signals; receive the audio and video signals transmitted by the TV modules and transmit the signals to the built-in 5G antenna after scrambling and modulation.
3	TV module	The TV module includes 8K decoding and image enhancing modules, which decode video images with different resolutions and enhance image quality and resolution. Different processing methods are adopted for contents in different formats: output 8K@60 Hz (or 8K@30 Hz) signals after decoding the contents of 8K video sources; output 8K@60 Hz (or 8K@30 Hz) signals after decoding the contents of 4K@60 Hz (or 4K@30 Hz) video sources and enhancing the resolution from 4K to 8K. In addition to processing image signals, the TV module also serves as the core in controlling the whole system by coordinating different modules of work in the system as well as the center of AIoT intelligent interaction.
4	FRC module	The module is used to increase the frame rate of 8K signals. The FRC module is used to increase the frame rate of the 8K signal when using 8K@120 Hz display with a TV module output signal of 8K@60 Hz or 8K@30 Hz and when using 8K@60 Hz display with a TV module output signal of 8K@30 Hz.
5	Camera and MIC module	Collect speech signals and image signals to realize AI man–machine interaction and AIoT control.
6	Built-in Wi-Fi and Bluetooth modules	8K TV holds the key to AIoT. The Wi-Fi and Bluetooth modules help realize the interconnection and intelligent interactive control between 8K TV and relevant AIoT devices.
7	8K display	UHD displays of 8K@60 Hz or 8K@120 Hz with 7680 × 4320 resolution that shows UHD video images.

interaction through AI speech and AI image. The smart devices include smart air conditioners, air purifiers, water purifiers, washing machines, kitchen ventilators, smart speakers and other Wi-Fi devices, smart home gateways, smart door locks, color temperature lights, smart switches, smart desk lamps, smart curtains, smoke sensors, emergency buttons, combustible gas alarms, and other ZigBee devices.

3.2 5G + VR/AR

Virtual reality (VR) and augmented reality (AR) are seen more frequently in scenarios, such as VR live broadcast and VR holographic theater at the 5G communication technology exhibition, scanning the character "fu" via AR on e-commerce platforms in the New Year, VR games, seeing apartments via VR, tourism intelligent interpretation and navigation via VR/AR, etc. 5G enables the quick integration of VR/AR into family life, and VR/AR products have become a new type of smart home product that helps boost family happiness.

3.2.1 *The concept and evolution of VR/AR*

VR technology uses computing devices to simulate a three-dimensional virtual world, providing users with a totally immersive experience through the simulation of vision, hearing, and other senses. AR is a new type of 3D technology that integrates information from the real world and the virtual world through a computer. The virtual information is simulated and applied in the real world, reaching people's sense organs and delivering a surreal sensory experience.

3.2.1.1 *Antique: The early form of VR/AR devices*

The first-ever VR device is "Sensorama" (1962) shown in Fig. 3.5. Users had to sit on a chair, put their heads into the device, and experience a virtual world through a sense of space created by a three-sided display. It is merely a simple 3D display tool for users.

In 1968, Ivan Sutherland, the father of computer graphics and VR and a famous computer scientist, designed the world's first head-mounted display "Sutherland", as shown in Fig. 3.6. However, due to technical limitations, the entire device was extremely heavy and could not function

70 *The World of 5G: Intelligent Home*

Figure 3.5 The world's first VR device "Sensorama".

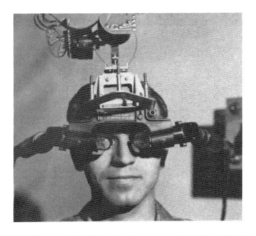

Figure 3.6 The world's first head-mounted display "Sutherland".

properly unless connected to the support rods on the ceiling. With its unique style, users half-jokingly called Sutherland the "Sword of Damocles" hanging over their heads.

From the 1980s to the 1990s, people have been picturing the arrival of VR. However, in 1991, a VR device called "Virtuality 1000CS" fully demonstrated something awkward about VR products for people at the time — they are heavy, expensive, and can only perform a single function. Although people pinned their hopes on VR, it is merely a concept.

3.2.1.2 *New home: The modern form of VR/AR devices*

In 2016, VR hardware met the requirements, and the VR all-in-one machine was put into production. The VR industry chain has taken shape with the involvement of equipment manufacturers and VR content providers. Capitalists spotted the opportunities and continued to inject vitality into the VR industry. The investment growth rate of the VR industry reached its peak, and the industry is embracing booming development.

Supported by 5G technology, all parties of VR industry chain and telecom operators have joined hands in accelerating the development of the VR/AR industry, and VR/AR products have become more portable and accessible. Today's mainstream VR all-in-one headset model is shown in Fig. 3.7.

With the commercialization of 5G networks, AR Ultra Short Throw (UST) glasses (Fig. 3.8) have been made available on the market. Instead of adopting a traditional battery design, the AR UST glasses use mobile phones as a mobile power source, and the 5G mobile network contributes to an immersive and comfortable AR experience.

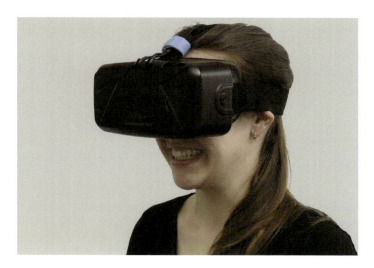

Figure 3.7   VR all-in-one headset model.

72 *The World of 5G: Intelligent Home*

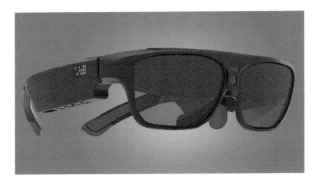

Figure 3.8   AR UST glasses model.

Mobile VR/AR applications in 5G networks will become powerful levers for social informatization and industrial intelligence. The introduction of 5G technology has given impetus to the development of VR/AR, which will facilitate the rapid advancement and implementation of VR/AR and further popularize VR/AR equipment from businesses to customers, so that VR/AR can transition from emerging technologies to home smart devices.

3.2.2   *Technological innovations that 5G brings to VR/AR*

Currently, most host VRs on the market adopt HDMI (high-definition multimedia interface), a wired connection, to transmit data, which is pricey and can only be used in a limited number of scenarios without free movement. Mobile VR is cheap and can be applied in multiple scenarios. Nevertheless, the Wi-Fi network coverage is limited and is susceptible to co-channel interference. Besides, the 4G network has insufficient bandwidth and high latency, causing network lag. Difficulties in transmission technology have become a bottleneck in the development of the VR/AR industry.

The high bandwidth of 5G meets VR/AR's strict requirements for network speed. The first stage of large-scale commercialization of 5G networks features enhanced mobile broadband (eMBB) scenarios, which are characterized by high bandwidth and low latency that guarantee VR/AR experience. The arrival of 5G communication technology will greatly boost the development of the VR/AR industry and reinvigorate the entire VR/AR industry.

3.2.2.1 *5G mobile edge computing technology: For "Fast" user experience*

Mobile edge computing (MEC) is a kind of network architecture that offers IT service environment and cloud computing capabilities at the edge of a mobile network and promotes network businesses to the wireless access network closer to users, which helps to realize low latency as well as a "fast" and "lag-free" experience, meeting the VR/AR users' needs. Typical applications that the European Telecommunications Standards Institute (ETSI) listed in the white book *Mobile Edge Computing-Key Technologies of 5G* include intelligent video acceleration and AR scenarios.

The MEC solution based on 5G architecture is shown in Fig. 3.9.

3.2.2.2 *5G Cloud render technology: For "Excellent" user experience*

High-quality VR/AR content is one of the key factors that promote industry consumption and boost market growth. Only high-end hardware with powerful computing power and graphics processing capabilities can satisfy high-quality VR/AR content rendering. 5G cloud render technology puts high-performance GPU processors in the cloud, reducing the

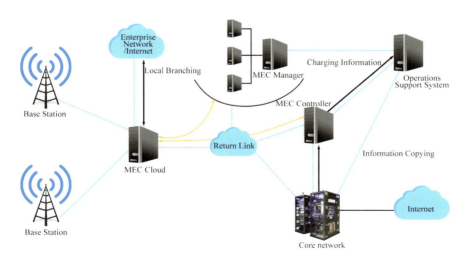

Figure 3.9 MEC solution based on 5G architecture.

computing pressure and complexity of terminal devices as well as terminal costs and ensuring terminal mobility and high-quality VR/AR content. VR/AR content service providers can manage content in real time on the cloud and provide users with a differentiated service experience.

3.2.2.3 5G UHD display technology: For "Clear" user experience

Thanks to 5G's ultra-reliable low-latency communication (uRLLC), 5G, with its ultra-high-definition and ultra-low-latency features and a tremendous improvement in eMBB rates, has become a coveted technology for developing UHD 4K/8K. The UHD image quality that determines users' dizziness also immerses them in a nearly real world. UHD 4K only represents the starting point of industry development. 8K or even a higher definition display technology is part of what the VR industry needs to explore in the future. VR/AR's requirements for processing pixels are multiplied, posing higher demands for video rendering. "UHD 4K/8K + 5G" will accelerate the promotion and implementation of VR/AR.

3.2.3 The future model of VR/AR in smart homes

VR is recognized by many giants as the "next general computing platform". With the brand-new way of interaction, VR devices can be turned into an interactive terminal for smart home systems in the future. When users play games while wearing a helmet and sweat profusely, the smart thermostat at home will adjust the temperature according to the user's body temperature, delivering a cooling experience. The above-mentioned scenarios will become a reality by taking smart home hardware devices as an operating platform and integrating them into VR.

The current combination of AR and smart home can enhance the sense of reality and make the experience even more realistic. For example, when it comes to home entertainment, AR devices can be integrated with intelligent audio and video entertainment systems, games, etc.

3.3 5G + Home Security

With the promotion and application of 5G technology, the further integration of 5G and home security is mainly embodied in video surveillance products represented by cameras and automatic sensing products represented by smart sensors. In the 5G era, the efficiency of data transmission has been tremendously improved, and the videos are available in real time with much clearer images, which has greatly promoted the development of video surveillance products. The wide-range connection of 5G has greatly expanded the scope of home security and supports the access of more smart sensors, thus generating monitoring data from more dimensions and perspectives. This has profound implications for the advancement of automatic sensing equipment.

3.3.1 *The origin and development of home security*

With the rapid development of the IoT technology, security equipment at home has evolved from single device to multi-device and from one-sided, sporadic monitoring to comprehensive systematic monitoring. Multiple sensors and automatic monitoring devices form a complete set of home security system with remarkable improvement in monitoring accuracy and efficiency. However, in the 4G era, most home security systems require passive monitoring and human intervention. Someone has to check abnormal situations detected in the system and take care of them to get the system back to normal. Since the entire system cannot respond autonomously, it is more like an automated system instead of an AI housekeeper. A real AI housekeeper is able to monitor the owner's circadian rhythm, travel routine, favorite placement methods and areas, as well as other personalized needs and make correct predictions, judgments, and active placements accordingly. It autonomously handles problems quite efficiently and safely without human intervention in the entire process. With the commercialization of 5G technology, the IoT and AI technology also witnessed greater development, so home security will gradually feature active monitoring, and an AI housekeeper will become a reality.

With the commercialization of 5G technology, we can insert a 5G card into the device and realize direct connection with the cloud through 5G technology, which enables faster and more stable data transmission in the home security system and a higher level of user experience without being affected by the Wi-Fi network environment.

3.3.2 *Home security applications and products*

The first line of defense in the home security system is the placement around the front door, which consists of smart cameras, etc. Currently, in most cases, this area adopts visual analysis and human feature recognition technologies, such as smart cat's eye, smart visual intercom, smart access control, and iris recognition. The second line of defense in the system uses smart sensors and other automatic sensing devices for placement in the rest of the house, including living rooms, bedrooms, kitchens, and balconies. These two lines of defense guarantee the security in home life, and a set of stable and sustainable family security systems can be built accordingly. Based on the two lines of defense, many classic and practical home security products have been made.

3.3.2.1 *Smart camera*

Existing cameras are inexpensive yet very functional. Even a hundred-yuan camera is able to shoot videos and pick up sound effect, becoming the "smart eyes and ears" that protect us in our home life. There are various types and styles of cameras on the market. Some common smart cameras are shown in Fig. 3.10. Popular smart camera brands include Hikvision, Dahua, Samsung, Sony, Panasonic, etc. There are a great variety of smart products made through camera-based integration, the most representative of which are smart cat's eye and smart visual intercom, which are described as follows:

(1) *Smart cat's eye*: The common smart cat's eyes have high resolution and a large optical lens. They are generally equipped with a series of

Figure 3.10   Common smart cameras.

highly practical security protection functions such as mobile detection, lingering alarm, and infrared night vision and support remote checking through mobile apps. We can also check the real-time situation in front of our house when we are away, and the infrared night vision feature allows us to check at night, which is fairly convenient and reassuring.
(2) *Smart visual intercom*: Smart visual intercom is a common device for image communication between homeowners and visitors in residential areas. Normally, it has a series of security features, such as camera shooting, call for opening the door, intercom, monitoring, night vision, and indoor unlocking. The intercom consists of two parts: host machine outside the door and indoor visual extension set. We can see the image of the visitors while talking with them through the extension set. After confirming the visitor's identity, we can press the unlock button or click the unlock button in the app to open the door remotely, which is relatively safe.

Smart visual intercom supports high-definition video conversations. In the 5G era with low latency and high bandwidth, the connection of video calls will be immensely improved. In the meantime, intercoms are economical and consume less energy, without wiring limitations; they can be easily accessed in the coverage area. Smart visual intercom further enhances the safety of home life.

3.3.2.2 *Smart sensor*

The so-called smart sensors are sensors with information processing features. Compared to ordinary sensors, smart sensors boast more prominent features, including but not limited to high-precision information collection, diversified functions, and automatic programming capabilities. The existing smart sensors are widely applied in home security, mainly in two areas, environmental monitoring sensing and security induction sensing.

Environmental monitoring sensors are mainly used to monitor changes in various environmental parameters in the house, including temperature, humidity, illuminance, smell, PM2.5 concentration, etc. The main environmental monitoring sensors include temperature and humidity sensors, illuminance sensors, smell sensors, and particulate matter sensors.

Security induction sensors are mainly used to protect family property and personal safety. They include all kinds of gas sensors, such as carbon monoxide sensor, VOC (volatile organic compounds) sensor, combustible gas sensor, and smoke sensor as well as door magnetic sensor, window magnetic sensor, sound sensor, and human body induction sensor.

3.4 5G + Home Network Equipment

3.4.1 *The development process of home networking devices*

Home networking devices emerged and developed along with the continuous development of the Internet. The birth of the Internet dates back to 1983 in the United States when the Department of Defense developed the TCP/IP protocol for heterogeneous networks. However, in the early days, the Internet was mostly applied in military and scientific sectors and not in households. It was not until the emergence of the World Wide Web (WWW) and Hypertext Markup Language (HTML) in 1990 that the Internet began to reach the ordinary users. In the meantime, home networking devices were available. The current mainstream home networking devices are optical fiber-based smart home gateways and Ethernet-based home routers. With the wider availability of 5G, 5G-based home networking devices are bound to thrive.

As the home Internet has witnessed an improvement from narrowband to broadband and from 100 Mb to gigabit, home networking devices have also gone through four stages of development, as shown in Fig. 3.11.

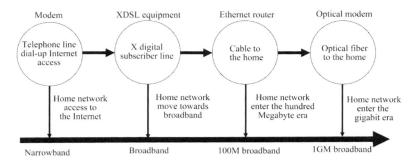

Figure 3.11 The four development stages of home networking devices.

3.4.2 Deficiencies in today's home networking devices

In the 30 years after its birth, the home Internet has gone through narrow-band, broadband, 100 MB, gigabit, and multiple other stages, and home networking devices have also evolved from the modems, xDSL equipment, and Ethernet routers in the early days to the recent home intelligent gateways. These devices by far enable Internet access to home networking users through a wired connection (telephone line, Ethernet, or optical fiber). There are two main reasons:

(1) *Technical reasons*: In the "Last Mile" of providing Internet access to users' homes, the corresponding wireless technology at each stage cannot meet access requirements like the wired technology of the same period. For example, normally the transmission distance of today's mainstream commercial optical fiber access network is 2–5 km (multimode optical fiber transceiver), and the maximum distance even reaches 20 km, with a stable downlink transmission rate of 1–10 Gb/s. Although the current mainstream commercial 4G has a transmission distance comparable to that of wired networks, the theoretical value of the network downlink rate is 100 Mb/s. While in real terms, 4G users' average download rate is about 20 Mb/s, far lower than that of wired networks.
(2) *Costs*: For network operators, the cost of wired network access per household is relatively low in densely populated areas. Since there are usually many households in the same building, what the operators have to do is to lay down the fiber-optic network in the building and then distribute it to each household through optical splitters. However, large-scale access of the wireless network including 4G in densely populated areas requires a tremendous increase in the number of base stations, which means an extremely high cost. Meanwhile, the home networking equipment has to be equipped with 4G transmission and receiving modules and the cost of which is much higher than that of the wired one.

For these reasons, although the household broadband is already widely used in the United States, Japan, South Korea, and other developed countries as well as in China, globally, the household broadband penetration rate remains less than 50%, and most of the families that have no access to broadband live in sparsely populated areas or areas with complicated geopolitical situations. For instance, the approval of land, right of way, and real rights in many countries are very difficult and wired access to the Internet through optical fiber and network cables is simply impossible.

3.4.3 *5G CPE realizes all-region coverage of home network*

Undoubtedly, the advent of 5G brings new opportunities to realize the all-region coverage of home networking equipment as the highest downlink rate of 5G is already comparable to that of the optical fiber. According to the definition of 5G key capability requirements by the International Telecommunication Union, 5G users can experience a rate as quick as 100 Mb/s–1 Gb/s, which is almost 10–100 times higher than that of 4G. This is not a technical problem. In addition, the connection density of 5G reaches 1 million units per square kilometer, a 10-fold increase compared to that of 4G, with a significant drop in the cost per unit. The equipment that combines 5G and home network is also called 5G CPE (Customer Premise Equipment). 5G CPE is a mobile signal access device that receives mobile signals and forwards them via Ethernet and wireless Wi-Fi signals. It can also be regarded as a device that converts high-speed 5G signals into Ethernet and Wi-Fi signals.

3.4.3.1 *5G CPE networking mode*

There are mainly two modes to connect a home to the Internet via the home networking equipment of 5G CPE: indoor networking and outdoor networking. These are described as follows:

(1) *Indoor networking mode*: In an indoor networking mode, 5G CPE is placed inside each home, and 5G CPE is directly connected to the 5G base station. This mode is applicable to densely situated family residences, as is shown in Fig. 3.12.

   In Fig. 3.12, 5G CPE is placed inside the user's home and is connected to the 5G core network through 5G signals and 5G base stations so as to connect the home to the Internet. Inside the user's home, 5G CPE can support several gigabit Ethernet interfaces and Wi-Fi wireless network interfaces.

Typical Applications of Smart Home–5G Integration 81

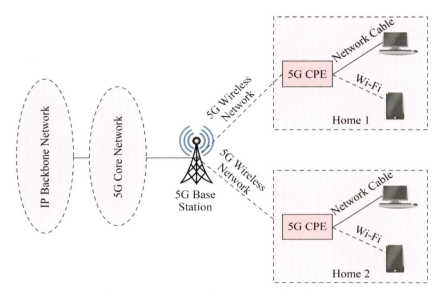

Figure 3.12   5G CPE indoor networking diagram.

(2) *Outdoor networking mode:* In an outdoor networking mode, the relay 5G CPE has to be placed outdoors and realize both providing Internet access to home users near the 5G CPE and completing 5G signal relay. This mode is applicable to scenarios where the residence is located far away from the 5G base station (usually more than 5 km), as is shown in Fig. 3.13.

In Fig. 3.13, Home 2 has weak or no signal as it is very far away from the 5G base station, yet Home 1 is relatively close to the base station, and Home 2 is not so far from Home 1. In this case, the 5G CPE of Home 1 that is placed outside the home is called a relay 5G CPE. The relay 5G CPE is connected to the 5G core network through the 5G base station, and Home 1 is connected to the Internet by connecting the Ethernet to the relay 5G CPE. Meanwhile, the relay 5G CPE relays the 5G signal so that one or more families can get access to the Internet through the relay 5G CPE that is placed inside the home.

3.4.3.2 *Typical 5G CPE*

A typical 5G CPE is shown in Fig. 3.14. Generally, 5G CPE has one to four downstream gigabit Ethernet ports, a power button, a USB debugging

82 *The World of 5G: Intelligent Home*

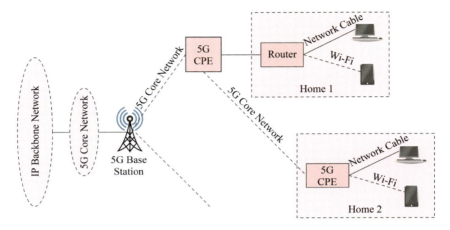

Figure 3.13 5G CPE outdoor relay networking diagram.

Figure 3.14 A typical 5G CPE.

port, a reset button, and several indicator lights. Moreover, both the 5G module and Wi-Fi module in the 5G CPE require larger-sized antennas, which seem higher in size, making it more convenient to arrange 5G and Wi-Fi antennas.

The technical characteristics of 5G CPE include mainly 5G access, Wi-Fi 6, and Mesh, which are described as follows:

(1) *5G access*: The 5G CPE uplink interface is connected via 5G wireless access instead of wired access like optical fiber or Ethernet. 5G

wireless access offers 5G CPE excellent mobile convenience. Meanwhile, the 5G network has high bandwidth, a peak rate of 10–20 Gb/s, and a user experience rate of 100 Mb/s–1 Gb/s. 5G CPE thus has a speed comparable to that of optical access. Compared to 5G mobile phones, 5G CPE can get access to the 5G network much faster as it has large-size antennas with stronger gains as well as stronger signals and higher access rate than that of mobile phones in harsh environments.

(2) *Wi-Fi 6*: The Wi-Fi of mainstream routers and home gateways continues to be Wi-Fi 5 or previous generations, yet 5G CPE supports Wi-Fi 6. Wi-Fi 6, also known as 802.11ax, represents the sixth generation or the latest wireless LAN technology. Compared to Wi-Fi 5, the previous generation, Wi-Fi 6 features faster speed, lower latency, and larger capacity; it is safer and saves more power. The maximum transmission rate of Wi-Fi 6 is 9.6 Gb/s, three times that of Wi-Fi 5; Wi-Fi 5 only supports downlink multi-user multiple-input multiple-output (MU-MIMO), while Wi-Fi 6 supports both uplink and downlink MU-MIMO, significantly reducing network congestion and latency; Wi-Fi 6 adopts orthogonal frequency division multiple access (OFDMA) technology, and each channel can transmit data very efficiently with a larger capacity; Wi-Fi 6 uses the safer WPA3 security protocol; Wi-Fi 6 applies the target wake time (TWT) technology that allows the device to plan communication time with the wireless router, saving time for wireless network usage and signal search, thus saving power for the device.

(3) *Mesh*: 5G CPE supports Wi-Fi Mesh, which is also called a wireless network or multi-hop network. The Mesh is mainly used to ensure Wi-Fi signal coverage in the home. For example, when 5G CPE is put in the hall and the Wi-Fi signal in a room several walls away from the hall is weak, installing a Mesh CPE in another room is adequate to do the trick. The customer end connects to the 5G CPE via Wi-Fi in the uplink and provides Wi-Fi access to other wireless devices via Wi-Fi in the downlink. The hot spot name of the Mesh customer end is exactly the same as that of the 5G CPE. Wi-Fi is available anywhere in the room and hall with the connected terminal, and the 5G CPE will automatically determine whether the Wi-Fi terminal is directly connected to 5G CPE or the Mesh customer end after interaction with the latter. The Mesh customer end and 5G CPE are usually equipped with larger-size Wi-Fi antennas, enabling a more stable Wi-Fi connection

84 The World of 5G: Intelligent Home

between the two. Meanwhile, the direction of these antennas can adjust dynamically based on the user's home environment, delivering the best user experience.

3.5 5G + Set-Top Box (STB)

In today's intelligent and digital world, digital set-top boxes provide digital video services to tens of thousands of households. However, digital set-top boxes require a high-speed and stable bandwidth based on wired networks, so from a global perspective, such services are not widely available as it is difficult and costly to install a cable in many regions of the world, especially in remote areas. Nevertheless, the 5G network has a high bandwidth and is easy to install, while 5G-based STB can meet the needs of these users.

3.5.1 *The origin and development of STB*

All the development stages of STBs are closely related to the advancement of digital and Internet technologies, from analog, one-way, SD, and IP technologies to digital, two-way, 4K, and smart technologies, as shown in Fig. 3.15.

The IP/smart STB networking is shown in Fig. 3.16. In the IPTV back-end server, BOSS (business operation support system) realizes features such as authentication and charging of STB businesses, and ITMS (integrated terminal management system) performs network management and server quality-related functions. In addition to BOSS and ITMS, there is also a special content delivery network (CDN). CDN is an intelligent

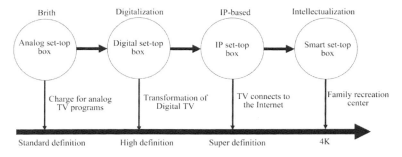

Figure 3.15 The four development stages of STB.

Typical Applications of Smart Home–5G Integration 85

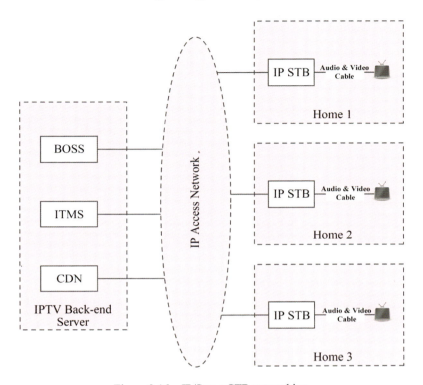

Figure 3.16 IP/Smart STB networking.

virtual network concurrently built on the basis of the existing network to process large-scale videos unique to IPTV STBs. CDN allows users to get access to needed contents nearby, reduce network congestion, and improve the response speed and hit rate of user access by relying on edge servers deployed in various places and through load balancing, content distribution, dispatch, and other functional modules in the central platform.

Figure 3.17 shows a typical smart STB. Smart STBs normally run on the Android system. The Central Processing Unit (CPU) uses a high-performance quad-core processor with a frequency of at least 2.0 GHz, integrates a high-performance multi-core graphics processing unit (GPU) with built-in 8 GB storage, 1 GB memory, and supports two USB 2.0, 10M/100M self-adaptive Ethernet, 2.4G/5.8G dual-band Wi-Fi and Bluetooth, as well as digital audio interface and a composite audio and video transmission port.

86 The World of 5G: Intelligent Home

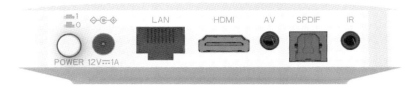

Figure 3.17   A typical smart STB.

3.5.2 *The coverage dead zone of STB*

Over more than three decades of development since its birth, the set-top box has developed from analog to digital, from one-way to two-way, from SD, HD to 4K UHD, and from cable (cable TV), IP to intelligence. So far, all the STBs must provide businesses through a wired connection (wired coaxial cable, optical fiber, or Ethernet).

As is known to all, the backbone network and metropolitan area network (MAN), among others, are built relatively fast, and the last mile to the user's home costs the most. In densely populated areas, the cost for the construction of the last mile per household is relatively low, while in sparsely populated areas such as the massive rural or mountainous areas, the average cost of installing and maintaining wired networks is very high. Therefore, although China now has 370 million broadband network users, globally, in many densely populated underdeveloped areas and massive sparsely populated areas, a lot of people have not yet been able to use smart TVs.

3.5.3 *Smart STB will be everywhere with the help of 5G*

In the past two years, major operators in many countries have stepped up efforts to build 5G base stations and promote the commercialization of 5G networks. According to the Ministry of Industry and Information Technology, as of the end of 2019, more than 130,000 5G base stations have been built across China, and it is expected that 2020 will see a tremendous increase in the number of newly built 5G base stations by the three major operators. There would be at least 680,000 5G base stations, according to a preliminary estimate. China Mobile is expected to offer 5G commercial services to Chinese cities at or above the prefecture level in 2020. As major operators keep pushing forward with 5G construction, it is expected that full coverage of 5G signals will be a reality in 2025.

For this reason, if the integration of 5G and smart STB enables the latter to access the Internet through 5G, then 5G's high bandwidth and low latency will be adequate to meet network bandwidth requirements of the smart STB's video-related services; with the gradually comprehensive coverage of 5G signals, many densely populated underdeveloped areas and massive sparsely populated areas will get access to STB. Why can't 4G do that? Although the maximum downlink peak value of a 4G network is 100 Mb/s, the average value in actual use is less than 20 Mb/s, failing to meet the bandwidth requirements of today's digital TV. While the theoretical peak value of 5G download speed is higher than 10 Gb/s, and the average speed is also above 100 Mb/s, sufficient to play today's and tomorrow's 4K/8K HD videos. Therefore, the birth and commercialization of 5G ensure the comprehensive coverage of smart STBs.

3.5.3.1 *5G STB networking*

Figure 3.18 shows the networking mode of 5G STB. The 5G STB is connected to the 5G core network through the 5G base station and then to the IP backbone network through the 5G core network before communicating

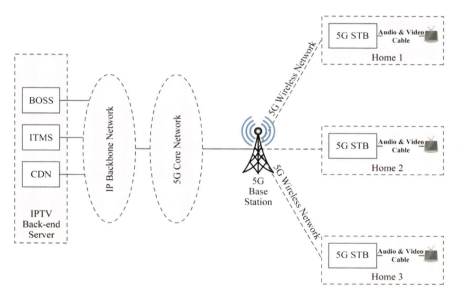

Figure 3.18   The networking mode of 5G STB.

with BOSS, ITMS, and CDN in the background of STB. With the help of 5G base stations, no wired network is needed in the last mile of the network between the base station and the user's home, making it much easier for the integration of 5G STB into many densely populated underdeveloped areas and massive sparsely populated areas without Internet access.

3.5.3.2 Typical 5G STB

The CPU of a typical 5G STB is an 8-core and 64-bit high-performance Cortex-A73 processor, integrated with a high-performance multi-core GPU (Mali-G52 MC6) and an independent NPU equipped with an engine with high computing power; it supports 8K@120 f/s decoding. 5G supports 5G NSA (Non-Standalone) and SA (Standalone) network architectures as well as telecommunication modes of multiple systems including 5G NR Sub6, FDD-LTE, TDD-LTE, and WCDMA. A SIM card should be inserted in a 5G module. The 5G module communicates with the CPU through PCI-e3.0 (third-generation Peripheral Component Interconnect Express) and USB 3.0 interfaces. A typical 5G STB is shown in Fig. 3.19.

The technical characteristics of 5G STB include mainly 5G access, 8K decoding, and AVS3.0, which are described as follows:

(1) *5G access*: The 5G STB has external antennas that allow the STB's 5G module to be connected to the 5G base station. The indoor 5G signal may be relatively weak, while the introduction of the external antenna would greatly improve the sensitivity of STB's 5G signal. According to the International Telecommunications Union's definition of 5G key capability requirements, the peak rate of 5G is 10 Gb/s,

Figure 3.19   A typical 5G STB.

the user experience rate is 100 Mb/s–1 Gb/s. Moreover, one million devices can be connected per square kilometer, with a minimum network delay of 1 ms and a flow density of up to 10 Mb/s per square meter. In the STB, the 5G module and the STB's CPU are connected through a PCI-e3.0 interface. According to the definition of PCI-SIG (PCI Special Interest Group), the PCI-e3.0 protocol supports 8.0 GT/s, which means each channel supports the transmission of 8G bits per second. The physical layer protocol of PCI-e3.0 uses a 128b/130b coding scheme, that is, 130 bits need to be sent for every 128 bits transmitted. In that case, each channel of the PCI-e3.0 protocol supports a rate of $8 \times 128/130 = 7.877$ Gb/s $= 984.6$ Mb/s. Besides, PCI-e3.0 can normally use multiple channels, and its transmission rate fully meets 8K ultra-clear video's requirements for bandwidth.

(2) *8K decoding*: Today's mainstream STBs are all 4K (4096×2160 pixels or 3840×2160 pixels, 4K refers to the screen resolution. With a resolution of 4096×2160 pixels, 4096 represents the pixel count in the horizontal direction, while 2160 represents the pixel count in the vertical direction) decoding, with 60 frames per second and an image depth of 10 bits. The 8K resolution has 7680×4320 pixels, with 120 frames per second and an image depth of 12 bits. With a resolution four times that of 4K TV, 8K delivers a much more immersive TV-watching experience with more lifelike images for the audience. Another advantage of 8K TV is its high peak brightness. Generally, the peak brightness of ordinary 4K TVs is about 1000 cd/m^2 at most, but that of an 8K TV can hit more than 4000 cd/m^2. Ultra-high peak brightness contributes to a wider overall dynamic range, and the light and shade would be more prominent in the more realistic pictures.

(3) *AVS3.0*: A video source with 8K@120 f/s needs to be compressed through efficient compression/coding methods to avoid a large bandwidth. The coding schemes suitable for 8K video sources are mainly H.266 and AVS3.0. H.266 standard is set by international companies such as Microsoft, Qualcomm, Samsung, Intel, Sony, Sharp, LG, Ericsson, as well as Huawei, and other Chinese companies. All the standards of video coding technology are supported by a vast number of technical patents. In general, there are 800–1000 patent families. Therefore, foreign companies take a larger part in the enterprises that set the H.266 standard, resulting in unorganized patent licenses and exorbitant costs that largely disrupted the industry development. AVS3.0 is a digital audio and video codec technical standard with

independent intellectual property rights in China. It was set by the Audio Video Coding Standard Workgroup of China (AVS Workgroup). Through the AVS3.0 coding technology, the code rate of 8K video source is effectively compressed to within 100 Mb/s, significantly saving network bandwidth. Today's 5G STBs adopt the AVS3.0 standard with independent intellectual property rights, which has epoch-making significance for the security of national technology, audio and video coding industry, as well as related enterprises.

3.6 5G + AIoT

3.6.1 *AIoT: From IoT*

As a bridge between AI IoT technology, 5G provides massive data support for AI technology, thereby facilitating the iteration of AI algorithms. Meanwhile, in the field of IoT, 5G technology can be applied in all smart devices, aside from mobile phones, and supports the access of an increasing number of smart devices. In the meantime, low latency also enables a quicker response of the IoT system. The emergence of AIoT and its relationship with 5G technology are shown in Fig. 3.20.

As is shown in Fig. 3.21, man and machine are interacting in new and different ways with the development of AIoT technology. In the era of PC Internet, man–machine interaction is based on the physical control through handles, buttons, and remote control. The era of mobile Internet has come in 2000 with the combination of mobile communication and the Internet. With the successive release of IOS and Android systems in 2007, mobile phones have become a major tool for communication, man–machine interaction can then be realized through touch panels and phone apps. The concept of AIoT was introduced in the industry in 2017, and man–machine interaction tended to be based on the basic ways of interaction between people, such as voice, movement, and vision. At this stage, with the rapid development of AI voice technology, the mode of man–machine interaction has expanded to include comprehensive voice control, including near-field voice control and far-field voice control. With the commercialization of 5G in 2019, 5G and AIoT technologies have been further integrated, and the mode of man–machine interaction would be extended to include remote control on the basis of machine vision. For example, control can be exercised through expression and gesture

Typical Applications of Smart Home–5G Integration 91

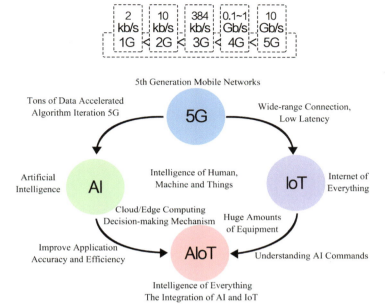

Figure 3.20 The emergence of AIoT and its relations with 5G technology.

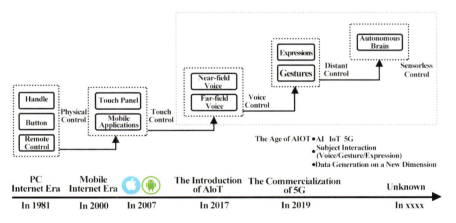

Figure 3.21 The development process of man–machine interaction mode.

recognition. In the near future, the interaction mode will be more thoughtful, and sensorless control based on the autonomous brain may even be realized.

In fact, it is obvious that in the evolving man–machine interaction modes, intelligent devices are constantly adapting to our usual ways of communication, making it easier for man–machine interaction, and smart life will be available to more users. Meanwhile, the ever-evolving man–machine interaction mode generated massive new dimensions of data, such as geographic locations and reading habits in the mobile Internet era. In the AIoT era, different dimensions of data such as the frequency of using voice commands and the number of online smart devices will also be recorded. Moreover, there may even be tons of new dimensions of data that were left unnoticed. Since data is the foundation and at the heart of AIoT development, these new dimensions of data have created unlimited possibilities for the development of AIoT2.

3.6.2 *AIoT: The future of intelligence of everything*

Over time, the era of single product intelligence featuring the device's independent response has passed for the development of AIoT. The era is characterized by the device's independent response to related commands, without a connection between devices, showing an evident islanding effect. We are currently in the era of connected intelligence where device connection provides a solid foundation for the introduction of scene intelligence, and the collaborative innovation capabilities between product chains have thus been greatly improved. Going forward, with the large-scale commercialization of 5G technology, it is predicted by industry insiders that AIoT will gradually enter the era of active intelligence with reduced communication cost between product ecological chains and efforts made on developing scene-based services. Meanwhile, the islanding effect will no longer exist. The AIoT system can actively record all of the user's personalized information, including behaviors, habits, hobbies, user portraits, home environment, etc. Through self-learning and training, the system is well prepared for 24 hours to provide users with corresponding scene-based services when appropriate.

At present, MarketsandMarkets, the world's second largest market research institute, predicts that globally, the AIoT market will continue to expand, with a 26% compound annual growth rate. It is estimated that the global AIoT market will exceed US$16 billion by 2024, with the highest average annual compound growth rate in the Asia-Pacific region. In the meantime, according to incomplete statistics provided by Wuzhen Think Tank, there are already more than 2,270 AIoT companies worldwide, and nearly a quarter of them are Chinese companies. This shows that AIoT has tremendous vitality and scalability in China, with immense untapped potential for growth. AIoT is also known as the "Intelligent Internet" and is regarded as a brand new growth point in the fourth wave of the world's information industry growth after the computer, the Internet, and the IoT.

AIoT also faces many challenges in its future development, as shown in Fig. 3.22. In terms of cloud computing, cloud computing capabilities determine the response speed and processing efficiency of the AIoT system, yet it relies on the breakthroughs in relevant key technologies such as servers, storage, cloud scheduling, and cloud terminals. Moreover, edge computing can enhance the device's local wake-up, remote speech noise reduction, and local recognition capabilities. However, the edge computing now has a weak foundation and is far from being popularized. As for the network, network quality directly affects the real-time performance and stability of the AIoT system. However, the current network is still confronted with serious interference and insufficient spectrum resources. AI is a distributed coordination mechanism between cloud computing and edge computing. It determines the important data that needs to be reported in time for processing in the cloud and the data that can be directly processed locally and skips the cloud. However, home-grown chips cannot meet the requirements of AI chips. Besides, AI model training takes a long

Figure 3.22 Challenges facing the development of AIoT.

time, with compatibility issues. When it comes to security, as the level of the IoT data index increases, data security still faces great challenges. As for standardization, an industry standard with universal recognition by the industry is yet to be set due to long AIoT ecological chain, different product forms, and serious isolated data island.

3.6.3 *Three applications of 5G and AIoT*

IoT aims to solve the underlying connection and data transmission problems, while AIoT focuses on the application of IoT's backend. In the future development of AIoT in the 5G era, 5G-related applications will be fully supported with 5G standard-based services, and traditional industries will be revolutionized through related applications that deeply integrate 5G and AIoT to break the old industry pattern and achieve all-round industrial upgrade.

At present, more and more companies are stepping into the AIoT field. The integration of 5G and AIoT technology will lead the technological trend in various aspects of the intelligent sector including cities, homes, manufacturing, transportation, medical care, office, tourism, etc. 5G and AIoT technology-related applications have also mushroomed, and visual Big Data platforms, IoT control systems, and scene-based services are the most common applications in a smart home.

3.6.3.1 *Visual Big Data platform*

Data is the foundation of AIoT applications as all AIoT applications make decisions based on data collection and analysis. Since the AIoT system works in real time, its data also continue to generate. These data include device-related information as well as key information of individuals or enterprise users. Visual Big Data access such useful data through AIoT-related technical interfaces, extract some key data indicators, such as the number of online devices and new devices, the distribution of voice usage and devices, the voice recognition rate, and the scenario execution rate, and display them in a visual manner to offer strategic technical support for the development of AIoT enterprises. This is, among others, the most common application of AIoT.

Data visualization is the beacon of AIoT development. It can provide a certain degree of intelligent assistance for enterprises to develop more applications, which is particularly important for the development of

AIoT-related enterprises. There are a variety of ways to display data in a visual way. Apart from the commonly used traditional pie charts, bar graphs, and line charts, multiple cool ways such as word clouds, waterfall charts, bubble charts, area charts, funnel charts, province maps, and GIS maps can be utilized. But generally, these AIoT data charts will be displayed based on the AIoT company's visual Big Data platform in whatever form, as shown in Fig. 3.23. Many AIoT companies, including Huawei, Haier, and Skyworth, have so far developed their own visual Big Data platforms.

3.6.3.2 *IoT control system*

In the field of smart home, IoT basically means the Internet of Everything, which connects devices in the household to realize some basic automatic control functions. While the nature of AIoT is the intelligence of everything, which integrates AI technology based on the IoT system for personalized, scene-based, and intelligent connection of household equipment that upgrades home automation to home intelligence to improve users' home life experience in an all-round way.

Home intelligence has to rely on a complete IoT control system. Currently, a uniformly recognized industry standard is yet to be developed in the field of AIoT as all AIoT companies are actively building AIoT ecosystems based on their own smart product forms and core competitiveness

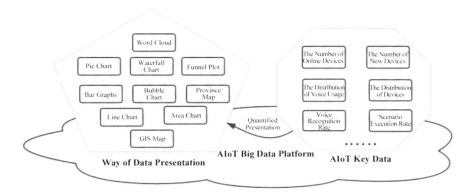

Figure 3.23 AIoT's visual Big Data platform.

96 *The World of 5G: Intelligent Home*

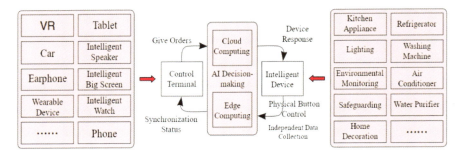

Figure 3.24 AIoT IoT control system.

and sparing no effort to build a unique IOT control system. A typical IoT control system is shown in Fig. 3.24. It is a set of control systems based on the integration and response of cloud computing, edge computing, control terminals, and smart devices. Based on AI's decision-making abilities, the control system determines whether the data is processed in the cloud or locally. The entire IoT control system is able to give orders, achieve cloud computing/edge computing, realize the artificial trigger control of the smart device response, as well as active data collection on the smart devices, edge computing/cloud computing, and autonomous perception control with information synchronization on the control terminal. Meanwhile, when users control the smart device through physical buttons, the state of the smart device is also synchronized to the control terminal, ensuring the real-time and uniform device state of the entire IoT control system.

At present, IoT control systems available in the market include the HiLink system developed by Huawei based on its own advantages in communication, Mijia system developed by Xiaomi based on its own IoT ecosystem, Swaiot OS developed by Skyworth with the support of over 40 million large screen TV users, JD Whale developed by JD based on the online open platform, Meiju developed by Midea based on its full-category home appliances, U-home system developed by Haier based on its smart home products, and many more.

3.6.3.3 *Scene-based services*

In the AIoT era, AI algorithms will be applied in more scene-based services. At the same time, AIoT-related scene-based services also provide

Typical Applications of Smart Home–5G Integration 97

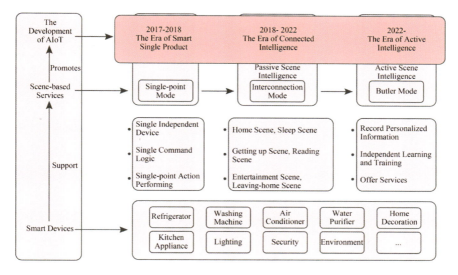

Figure 3.25 The development of AIoT scene-based services.

strong support for AI algorithms through data, especially those collected from scene-based services, which in turn will further accelerate the iteration of AI algorithms, thereby realizing smart home life. Therefore, in the field of smart homes, AIoT will be mainly applied in scene-based services, etc.

With the continuous development of AIoT technology, scene-based services are showing more new forms, as shown in Fig. 3.25. The massive number of smart devices in the AIoT system offers strong support for smart services. The single-point mode of the device represents the early form of scene-based services. For example, a single voice command is given through a smart speaker to control the switch of the corresponding independent device at a single point. Interconnectivity between devices enables the control of multiple terminal responses through cloud computing or edge computing, and scene-based services are upgraded to an interconnection mode. At this moment, the scenes are mostly passive ones that need to be set in advance. For instance, when the user is going to take a rest, a command like "I'm going to sleep" can be given for home devices to perform according to what has already been set in the sleep scene: non-essential equipment and curtains will automatically close, lights will gradually turn off, etc. With its commercialization, 5G technology will greatly unleash cloud AI capabilities, AIoT will enter the era of active intelligence, and scene-based services will be turned into a butler mode with mostly active scenes. Moreover, the execution in the AIoT system will actively record all of the user's personalized information instead of depending on the user's voice scene instructions. Then the system teaches and trains itself and is on standby for 24 hours to actively provide users with corresponding scene-based services when appropriate.

With the development of sensor technology and the advent of the 5G era, more companies will provide more customer-friendly scene-based services, and the intelligent experience of home life will be further improved.

Chapter 4

Innovative Products Integrating Smart Home and 5G

4.1 Intelligent Home System

4.1.1 *A new definition of the 5G smart home system*

Under the premise of accelerated popularization of 5G, in the future home scene, all smart home appliances can be connected to the network, connected to the server, and integrated into the big scene of the IoT through 5G. On the basis of good coverage and large bandwidth of 5G network, on the one hand, it can solve the problems of poor experience, such as disconnection of equipment and network lag, which are common in the current smart home. On the other hand, it can also enable the family to carry out wireless protocol conversion through 5G, so that the family has good wireless network coverage to meet the wireless network connection needs of various types of smart home appliances.

The smart home system is one of the important links; through the smart home system, home appliances will be intelligent, networked, and can be interconnected. The interactive experience between people and home appliances can be more diverse. At the same time, the smart home system has the basic characteristics of health, convenience, comfort, safety, and energy-saving to meet people's pursuit of a better life.

The smart home system can promote the realization of the vision of a better life with science and technology, so the design of a smart home system needs to consider the compatibility and cross-system compatibility and other issues. Generally speaking, a complete smart home system should have the following three characteristics:

(1) *Advanced and feasible*: An intelligent home system is a home network system based on an intelligent home environment. It combines high-tech digital technology, network communication technology, IoT communication technology, AI technology, etc. Especially, in audio and video, the advanced codec technology and compression technology are adopted to realize real-time dynamic transmission of audio and video signals.
(2) *Openness and standard*: The architecture of the smart home system is based on the interconnection technology standard in the industry, which can provide a platform to realize the interconnection and control of different manufacturers and different appliances. At the same time, considering the real-time operation of the intelligent terminal system and that it is closely related to the lives of users, in order to ensure the long-term and stable operation of the products, the intelligent terminal series products are developed with compatibility. The subsequent listed products can directly replace the existing products and achieve the same functions.
(3) *Scalability and easy maintainability*: Considering the upgrading of network technology and customer demand and the standard logical architecture of the smart home system design, without upgrading the software and hardware of the indoor intelligent terminal, it can be easily extended and connected to other systems in the family or even the community, such as parking system and meter reading system, through the standard interface of the server, according to the later development needs of the property and users.

4.1.2 *Architecture scheme of the intelligent home system*

As shown in Fig. 4.1, the overall control and software architecture of the smart home system can be vertically divided into four levels from the underlying technology to the application, namely, the device access layer, the edge processing layer, the cloud platform layer, and the application service layer.

4.1.2.1 *Device access layer*

The device access layer contains information about the equipment and collects different types of intelligence, such as intelligent household appliances,

Innovative Products Integrating Smart Home and 5G 101

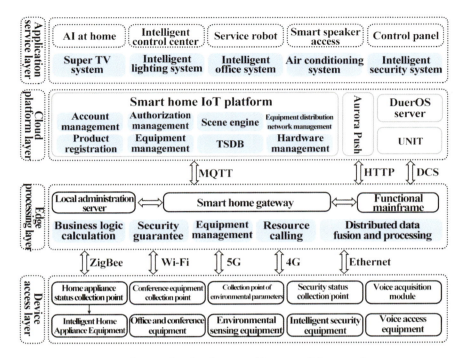

Figure 4.1 Overall control and software architecture of the smart home system.

office and conference equipment, environmental sensing devices, as well as intelligent security and access equipment and through a variety of network communication methods, connects with the upper level, including near-field communications (such as ZigBee, Wi-Fi, Bluetooth, RFID, and NFC), long-distance wireless networks (e.g., 5G, 4G, 3G, GSM, GPRS, and GPS), and cables (such as Ethernet and Fieldbus).

4.1.2.2 *Edge processing layer*

In order to make up for the deficiency of centralized cloud computing, the concept of edge computing came into being. It refers to a distributed open platform that integrates the core capabilities of the network, computing, storage, and application on the edge of the network near the physical terminal or data source, and provides edge intelligent services for the underlying intelligent terminal devices. Common edge processing devices include smart home gateways, local management servers, and functional hosts, which provide services such as business logic calculation, security assurance, device management, resource invocation, distributed data fusion, and processing for the bottom layer.

4.1.2.3 *Cloud platform layer*

Cloud platform layer can provide cloud services through the cloud computing center. It mainly includes its own smart home IoT platform and third-party service provider platform (such as voice service platform) and provides account management, authorization management, scene engine, device distribution network management, product registration, device management, TSDB (timing database), hardware management, and other services for the lower level. All the data are transmitted to the cloud computing center for processing through the network, so that the resources can be highly centralized and integrated, equipping the cloud computing IoT platform with high versatility.

4.1.2.4 *Application service layer*

As shown in Fig. 4.2, a typical application of a smart home system service mainly includes a total of 10 scenarios (including five function subsystems and three categories). People can interact with each other through a variety of intelligent control centers, service robots, mobile apps, or voice

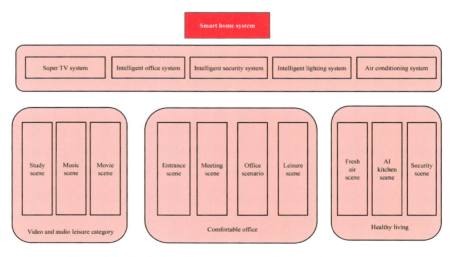

Figure 4.2   Typical application services of a smart home system.

interaction and enjoy the comfortable and convenient service experience brought about by the smart home system.

4.1.3 *Composition analysis of the intelligent home system*

The smart home system brings together the new generation of AI image quality enhancement technology, accurate voice recognition technology, human body multiple sensing technology, comfortable environment analysis technology, intelligent remote control technology, and new network communication fusion technology for the needs of a high-quality home life that combines health technology. The five intelligent functional subsystems of a typical smart home system are super TV system, intelligent office system, intelligent security system, intelligent lighting system, and air conditioning system, presenting a unique intelligent interactive experience.

4.1.3.1 *Super TV system*

As shown in Fig. 4.3, a super television system includes the television, Dolby sound, light effect, and motor control. All devices are managed

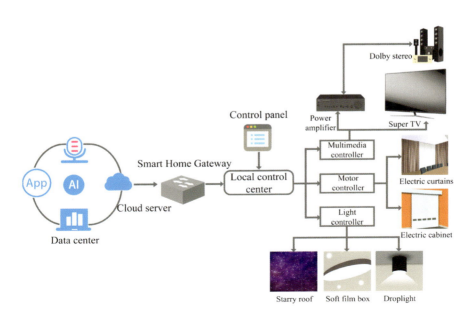

Figure 4.3 Block diagram of the super TV system.

intelligently through the local control center, with two management modes of on-site control panel control and remote control through the cloud server, providing customized video and audio entertainment experience for high-end users. In the scene display, through the linkage of sound, light, and electricity, it provides a shocking and relaxing immersive new experience, featuring four characteristics: high-quality painting, beautiful sound quality, good intelligence control, and high appearance level.

4.1.3.2 *Intelligent office system*

As shown in Fig. 4.4, the intelligent office system, through the scene linkage between multimedia, intelligent products, lighting, security, and other equipment, can realize the collaborative intelligent office of local end and remote end, bringing people a comfortable, convenient, intelligent, and other multi-dimensional office experience. The intelligent office system has the functions of park monitoring, real-time tracking of information flow, remote meeting, online marking, speech recognition and text conversion, file sharing, etc.

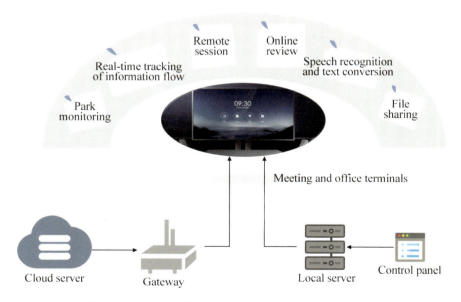

Figure 4.4 Block diagram of the intelligent office system.

Innovative Products Integrating Smart Home and 5G 105

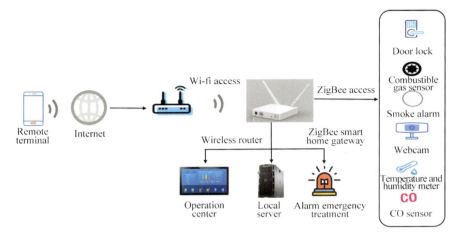

Figure 4.5　Block diagram of the intelligent security system.

4.1.3.3 *Intelligent security system*

The intelligent security system includes kitchen and bathroom life security and office security, as shown in Fig. 4.5. A variety of front-end detectors are connected to the smart home gateway through ZigBee, and the local server and operation center are centrally controlled. Alarm emergency processing channels are designed to deal with emergencies. Remote terminals can also be monitored and managed through the Internet.

4.1.3.4 *Intelligent lighting system*

The intelligent lighting system can be applied in multiple theme spaces such as healthy kitchen, comfortable office, super video and audio, as shown in Fig. 4.6. Different types of lights are controlled by the light control module, which communicates with the local host through the Fieldbus or local gateway. The back end can close the lights and adjust the brightness jointly according to different application scenarios. The whole intelligent lighting system brings people an immersive and comfortable experience through situational light changes.

4.1.3.5 *Air conditioning system*

As shown in Fig. 4.7, the air conditioning system consists of an air conditioning unit, a fresh air unit, and a humidifier. Through turbine

106 *The World of 5G: Intelligent Home*

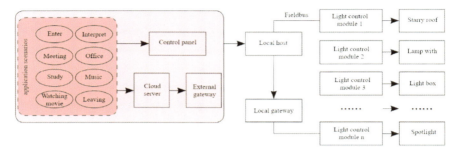

Figure 4.6 Block diagram of the intelligent lighting system.

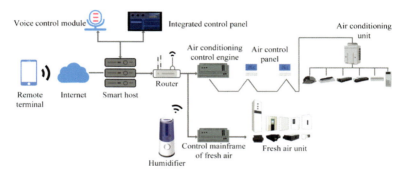

Figure 4.7 Block diagram of the air conditioning system.

self-suction air purification, local voice control, in-depth analysis of user habits, and other technologies, real-time perception of the field environment and automatic adjustment of temperature, wind speed, air quality, and humidity can be realized, with air self-cleaning, human comfort sensing, intelligent voice control, and other features.

4.1.4 *New interactive experience of the smart home system*

4.1.4.1 *Video and audio leisure application scenes*

The video and audio leisure application of the smart home system combines the large-size super TV technology and Dolby panoramic sound 7.1.4 technology as well as the lighting interaction effect such as starry roof, to meet people's life needs for video and audio leisure and bring a new comfortable experience of immersive sound and vision to people.

Innovative Products Integrating Smart Home and 5G 107

Figure 4.8 Three application scenes of video and sound leisure.

Video and audio leisure applications include three characteristic application scenarios, as shown in Fig. 4.8:

(1) *Scene of the study*: In the study scene, the control center will be triggered to control the multimedia, motor, and lighting. The TV, power amplifier, and Dolby stereo are closed, the bookcase door and electric curtain are opened, and the lighting is adjusted to 70% brightness. The study scene adopts the bionic breathing starry roof technology, the soft film light box simulates the real natural scenery outside the window, the automatic bookcase co-moves, and the lighting scene changes adaptively, bringing people a comfortable and relaxed reading environment.

(2) *Music scene*: In the music scene, the control center will be triggered to control the multimedia, motor, and lighting. The TV is turned off, the power amplifier is selected to the blue light signal source, the Dolby stereo is turned on, the bookcase door is closed slowly, the electric curtain is opened, and the light is adjusted to 30% dim brightness. The music scene adopts Dolby Panorama 7.1.4 sound channels, the natural light sense is adjusted to the comfortable brightness of

108   *The World of 5G: Intelligent Home*

human eyes, and the bookcase displays beautiful decorations, bringing immersive auditory enjoyment.
(3) *Movie scene*: In a movie scene, a control center is triggered to control the multimedia, motor, and lighting. Among them, the TV is opened, the power amplifier is selected to the TV signal source, the Dolby sound is opened, the bookcase door is closed, the electric curtain is closed, and all the lights are switched off in turn. The door of the TV cabinet opens slowly with the picture, showing the all-around visual and auditory experience such as super TV picture quality, sound quality, and Dolby panoramic sound in the dark.

4.1.4.2 *Comfortable office application scene*

The comfortable office exhibition hall of the smart home system displays various features such as intelligent office, convenient office, safe office, and comfortable office through entry experience, multi-functional conference, and scenario-oriented display of the smart office. Comfortable office applications include four characteristic application scenes, as shown in Fig. 4.9:

(1) *Entry scene*: In the entry scene, through the use of a number of accurate sensing technologies and AI identity recognition technology, the linkage of light and music of entry mode is automatically triggered with scene self-adaptation. When the infrared sensor senses a person coming in, it will trigger the control of the infrared control module, motor control module, and relay switch module. When the projector is off, the music will be turned on. The electric curtain will be opened and raised to 70%, the ceiling soft film light box and the lighting will be adjusted to 70% brightness, and the photochromic glass will become transparent.
(2) *Meeting scene*: In the multi-function meeting scenario, the control of infrared control module, motor control module, and relay switch module will be triggered. The meeting screen will be opened, music will be turned off, the electric curtain will be closed, the soft film ceiling light boxes and lighting will be adjusted to 70% brightness, and the color-changing glass will be turned off and blurred, building a suitable atmosphere for a meeting. It can meet many efficient meeting functions, such as remote meeting, speech audio to text, large screen whiteboard, monitoring alarm, and data display on a large screen in the park.

Innovative Products Integrating Smart Home and 5G 109

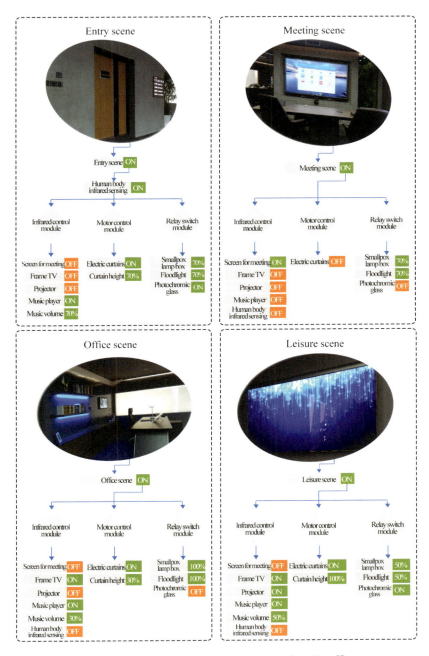

Figure 4.9 Four application scenes of comfortable office.

110 *The World of 5G: Intelligent Home*

(3) *Office scene*: In the comfortable office scene, the control of infrared control module, motor control module, and relay switch module will be triggered. Meeting screens will be turned off, music will be turned on, electric curtains will be opened and raised to 30%, ceiling soft film light boxes and lighting will be adjusted to 100% brightness, and the color-changing glass will be turned off and blurred, creating a comfortable office environment.

(4) *Leisure scene*: In the leisure scene, it will trigger the control of the infrared control module, the motor control module, and the relay switch module. The conference screen will be closed, the frame TV will be turned on to play artistic leisure pictures, the music will be turned on, the electric curtain will be opened and raised to 100%, the ceiling soft film light box and the lighting will be adjusted to 50% brightness, and the color-changing glass will be opened to become transparent, bringing people a leisurely and relaxed scene experience.

4.1.4.3 *Healthy living application scene*

The kitchen, as a healthy area for home eating, is an important scene for home living. Combined with the cutting-edge technology of kitchen electricity products, the smart home system shows the theme of "comfortable, safe, and convenient living" in the smart kitchen. The application of healthy life includes three characteristic application scenes, as shown in Fig. 4.10:

(1) *Fresh air scene*: The air system is an important part of life and home. Combined with body sensing and on-site sensing technology, it creates a comfortable experience of fresh air in the kitchen space. In the fresh air scene, the data processing center will communicate with the air quality module, air conditioning control module, and humidity detection module, so as to issue adjustment instructions to the fresh air unit, air conditioning unit, and humidifier and transmit the perceived data to the data processing center to create an air fresh scene suitable for home furnishing.

(2) *AI kitchen scene*: The AI kitchen combines the latest kitchen electricity product technology to bring people the experience of a smart kitchen through voice entry, touch control, and other ways. The kitchen TV is mainly used as the main control center, which can be operated jointly with home appliances with screens, such as range hoods and refrigerators, and can also be used to control small kitchen

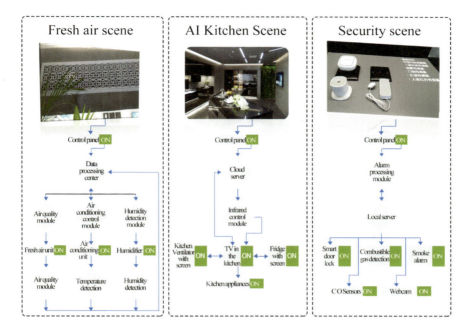

Figure 4.10 Three application scenes of healthy living application.

appliances without screens. All household appliances can be remotely controlled and scenarized through the cloud server, creating a new experience of AI kitchen.

(3) *Security scene*: In the security scene, smoke alarm, combustible gas detector, CO sensor, smart door lock, webcam, and so on can be used for home detection and warning. It can deal with emergencies through the local server in time and can synchronize the alarm information to the management center and can also be sent to the mobile phone or office intelligent terminal remotely, so that people can always monitor the safety state of the home even from a distance and realize the home safety of the kitchen life.

4.2 Intelligent Control Center

4.2.1 *New demand for 5G intelligent control center*

4.2.1.1 *Demand for new intelligent control centers*

At present, although the concept of smart home and related products have experienced decades of development, in the vast real estate market in

China, the penetration rate is still not particularly high. One important reason is that the smart home does not have a good intelligent control center for interaction. The function of the smart home control solutions of different manufacturers presented the characteristic of "fragmentation". At present, smart home-related products are simply combined with multiple independent functions. Whether it is the purpose of explanation, demonstration, or family use of the product, it is difficult for consumers to understand the concept of the product and smart home, let alone directly buy the product. Therefore, the first thing that the smart home should solve is the problem of "fragmentation" of experience.

At present, mobile phones, televisions, and smart speakers, which may be used as intelligent control centers, cannot provide convenient control methods and interactive means. At the same time, due to the inherent defects of mobile phones, such as privacy needs which require improvement, it is not suitable for the control center of the family nor is it suitable for integrating more functions in the control center. In addition to the smart home scene, a variety of scenes including hotel scene, office scene, education scene, conference scene, etc., currently do not have a control center scheme widely accepted by users.

4.2.1.2 *A new generation of intelligent control center*

With the development of society, people's requirements for the living environment have been significantly improved, and higher requirements have been put forward for the quality of life. They are also more inclined to a healthy, convenient, comfortable, safe, and energy-saving lifestyle. The development of modern technology has also greatly raised the standard of quality of life in the future. It is hoped that a new intelligent control center product will provide a simpler way to control appliances and scenes inside the home to meet the needs of education, leisure, social, and service while at the same time being able to connect to the mobile phone ecosystem to some extent. For example, in the office environment, people pay more attention to socializing, education, and working; in the hotel scene, people may pay more attention to leisure and service; in the traffic scene, people pay more attention to realize the interconnection between the vehicle and the family and realize the remote control of the home in the car.

At present, the market has emerged with integrated control function of the intelligent control center products. As the control center of intelligent equipment and intelligent electrical appliances in life, intelligent control center products can well improve the user experience and increase the use of the scene. It can also comprehensively change the impact of the modern home system on life from multiple aspects such as use scenario, use mode, and interconnection and introduce the concepts of convenience, comfort, safety, health, and energy-saving into the new experience of the smart home system.

4.2.2 *Intelligent control center with a fixed form*

4.2.2.1 *Function requirements of an intelligent control center with a fixed form*

A fixed form of intelligent control center will often be applied in the home, hotel, or office. These places are often strict in decoration style as a whole. At the same time, in order to prevent the phenomenon of consumer habits of sudden control equipment damage, the intelligent control center with the fixed form can choose to be combined with traditional furniture tea table (Fig. 4.11), which provides fixed control in the form of fixed screen, realizing the expansion of the scope of control and use of the intelligent control center and avoiding the inconvenience caused by private equipment as a control center. The intelligent control center and traditional furniture tea table with the fixed form are perfectly integrated into many scenes, such as home, hotel, and office.

Figure 4.11 Two kinds of intelligent control centers with the fixed form which are combined with tea tables.

Some of the newest intelligent control centers offer multiple modes of operation. Compared to smartphones, newly introduced intelligent control centers adopt the public operating mode. This makes it convenient for family members, meeting members, or hotel guests to apply the smart home system, avoiding the situation in which users need to carry out account matching and other cumbersome operations to obtain the control system access in the case of a smartphone as an intelligent control center. When operating the intelligent control center, users can touch the control panel to select entertainment, education, social, office, shopping, life, and other control modes for the input port. More information can be obtained through the screen display and screen touch to meet more use scenes, and the operation is more convenient.

The primary function of the intelligent control center is to control the home appliances of the whole house, including intelligent home appliances connected to the Internet and non-intelligent home appliances that support infrared control as well as intelligent devices that support wireless charging. At the same time, as the control center of the home, the intelligent control center also contains a touch panel for human–computer interaction. The functions of a typical intelligent control center are shown in Table 4.1.

4.2.2.2 Hardware architecture of the intelligent control center with a fixed form

In order to achieve all the functions of the intelligent control center, to meet the various needs of the users, and to adapt to the different scenes (such as entertainment scene, leisure scene, office scene, and other scenes), the intelligent control center with a fixed form generally contains the following hardware function modules: core control motherboard module, network communication module, wireless charging module, built-in speaker module, infrared control module, voice acquisition module, touch panel module, built-in freezer module, and the cloud server module. The overall architecture and interaction mode of the intelligent control center with fixed form are shown in Fig. 4.12.

The functions of all modules of the intelligent control center are as follows:

(1) *Core control motherboard module*: As the core control component of the intelligent control center, the control motherboard is connected

Table 4.1 Function and introduction of an intelligent control center.

Serial number	Functional properties	Function introduction
1	Home appliance control function	Through AIoT, apps and hardware can be controlled, far-field voice can be supported, and intelligent control of multi-brand and multi-category electrical appliances can be realized
2	Intelligent voice function	Intelligent voice recognition, voice interaction with users, information retrieval, and control of home appliances
3	Touch panel interaction function	With the large touch screen and the built-in open Android system, users can freely download related apps according to their own habits and needs, and various functions such as security and painting can be realized
4	Wireless charging function	It supports fast charging of wireless charging devices to improve the convenience of mobile phone use
5	Educational and entertainment function	Entertainment, education, news and other interactive content can be integrated and displayed on a large screen
6	Live TV function	Sports events, real-time news, and other TV programs live broadcast function
7	Music playback function	With the sound system, users can play their favorite music at any time
8	Freezer storage function	According to the items stored in the freezer, the operation mode of the freezer can be switched with one key

with other modules and communicates with the wireless charging module, the built-in speaker module, the voice acquisition module, the touch panel module, and the built-in freezer module in the intelligent control center through a wire. The control motherboard can store the user's inputted data and the operating system of the intelligent control center with digital storage. The control motherboard has a wireless communication function, which can not only realize the interaction of each module of the intelligent control center and obtain network resources but also control the intelligent home appliances in the intelligent control center through the network in the way of cloud-to-cloud docking.

116 *The World of 5G: Intelligent Home*

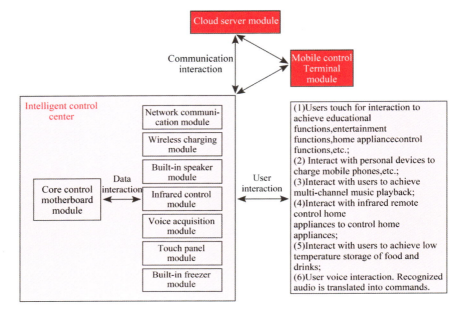

Figure 4.12 The overall architecture and interaction mode of the intelligent control center with a fixed form.

(2) *Network communication module*: The network communication module realizes the interaction between the core control motherboard module and the Internet through Wi-Fi, Bluetooth, ZigBee, mobile cellular network, and other forms, realizes the upload and download of information, as well as the Internet functions of the touch panel module and other modules.

(3) *Wireless charging module*: The wireless charging module is designed to join the intelligent control center, placed under the surface of the intelligent control center in a hidden way, and connected to the control motherboard through a wired way. The wireless charging module wirelessly transmits the electric energy controlling the motherboard to the devices placed above the wireless charging module, such as mobile phones. Without affecting the appearance of the intelligent control center, common devices such as mobile phones can be charged to improve the convenience of life.

(4) *Built-in speaker module*: The built-in speaker module includes the Dolby channel system, with five or more channels built in a

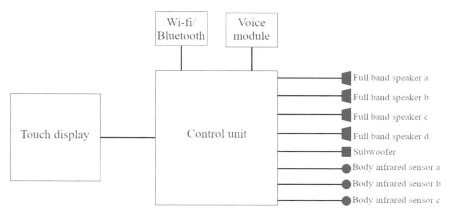

Figure 4.13 Multichannel built-in speaker module architecture.

hidden way. The built-in speaker module interacts with the core control motherboard module through a wire, so that the audio signal is transmitted to the built-in speaker module and the music playback function is realized. Figure 4.13 shows the multi-channel built-in speaker module architecture. The five speakers consist of four full-frequency speakers and one bass speaker. The four full-frequency speakers are oriented in the positive direction and the opposite direction of the intelligent control center, respectively. The bass speaker is located in the middle of the intelligent control center and in the downward direction. The five speakers are connected to the main control unit of the intelligent control center. There are three human body infrared sensors in the front, rear, and left of the intelligent control center. The system can judge the position of the person sitting through the infrared sensor of the human body, so as to intelligently adjust the direction of the sound channel and the display screen.

(5) *Infrared control module*: At present, the new intelligent devices connected to the users' homes are all intelligent devices with chips that can be connected to the IoT. They use RFID, wireless data communication, and other technologies to automatically identify items and interconnect and share information. However, for the existing home appliances with built-in infrared control function of traditional non-intelligent devices, a new generation of intelligent control center integrated with a variety of communication methods also contains the

infrared control module in order to achieve the control of traditional home appliances.

(6) *Voice acquisition module*: The voice acquisition module is integrated into the intelligent control center with modular design to realize the interaction with users by voice. The voice acquisition module is connected to the control motherboard through a wire, and the user's voice is collected and submitted to the control motherboard. The intelligent control center (after integrating the voice acquisition module) is not only the control center of intelligent devices but also the video and audio entertainment center, which can respond to voice interaction, watch video, listen to music, play games, and provide entertainment at any time.

(7) *Touch panel module*: The surface of the touch panel is covered with touch glass, which can not only protect the screen but also realize the touch interaction of the touch panel through the capacitive medium. The touch panel communicates with the control board by means of wired communication and can control the household appliances through the control software. By connecting to the Internet through the control of the motherboard to download the required applications, users can realize a variety of applications run on the interactive interface. Popular applications such as chess and card games and WeChat and Douyin can be installed to realize family entertainment and social networking. Users can also install education programs to realize the education of family teenagers.

(8) *Built-in freezer module*: The built-in freezer module (Fig. 4.14) is incorporated into the intelligent control center in a modular design. The built-in freezer module communicates with the core control motherboard module through the data bus and can switch the operating modes of the freezer with one key. All modes can provide the corresponding temperature and humidity in the cabinet. As storage equipment, the built-in freezer can provide a suitable environment for storing fruits, drinks, tea, or wine.

(9) *Cloud server module*: The voice uploaded to the network by the core control motherboard module is analyzed through the cloud server module to obtain the meaning of the user's voice information, and then the analysis results are transmitted to all modules to realize the command delegation and meet the user's language control needs. The voice acquisition module can provide a convenient interactive mode, allowing users to control the intelligent home devices connected with

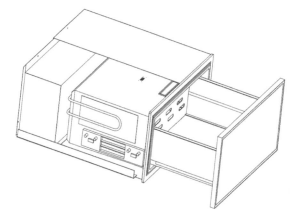

Figure 4.14 Built-in freezer module.

the intelligent control center through voice without touch control. At the same time, the cloud server learns and records the user's habits, usage patterns, and necessary user information, so as to better provide users with a good user experience and realize intelligent interaction mode.

4.2.2.3 *The interaction mode of the intelligent control center with a fixed form*

In the home environment, hotel environment, or office environment, the household appliances are controlled through the intelligent control center with a fixed form. The process is shown in Fig. 4.15. First of all, users input commands in the intelligent control center with a fixed form, and the input methods can be divided into touch operation on the touch panel or voice command operation. When the intelligent control center successfully collects the command, the user command will be transmitted to the core control motherboard module, and the core control motherboard module is responsible for analyzing the command. If the command issued is a home appliance control command, the type of home appliance to be controlled would be judged. If the home appliance to be controlled is an intelligent device, the relevant command is uploaded to the cloud server through the network communication module of the intelligent control center, and the home appliance is reached through the cloud server under

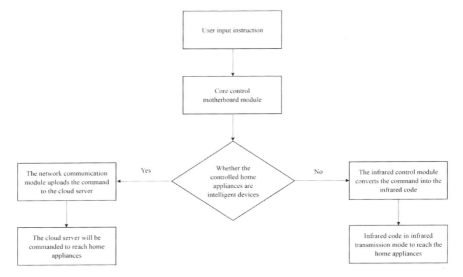

Figure 4.15 The process of the intelligent control center with a fixed form to control the household appliances.

the command. If the home appliances to be controlled are not intelligent devices, the intelligent control center will transmit the command to the infrared control module, which will convert the command to the infrared code and issue the command to the home appliances in the way of infrared transmission.

4.2.3 *Intelligent control center with a mobile form*

Although the intelligent control center with a fixed form integrates into the family life with its excellent appearance, its main application scene is in the living room. In other parts of the room or even outdoors, it is not convenient to use the intelligent control center with a fixed form. Therefore, in the overall scheme of the intelligent control center, in addition to the fixed form of the intelligent control center, the mobile form of the intelligent control center is also needed to facilitate portability so as to be used in various scenes.

Due to its powerful functions, the mobile phone has been defined by many manufacturers as the mobile intelligent control center of the family.

However, due to privacy requirements, the mobile phone is often not suitable for sharing among family members. Therefore, mobile intelligent control centers that can be truly accepted by families usually provide mobile control services in the form of tablet computers or intelligent remote controls, as shown in Fig. 4.16.

The intelligent control center in the mobile form is attached to the whole intelligent control center solution system in the form of mobile control. At the same time, it is also an independent device that can control household appliances and interact with users. Therefore, the mobile form of the intelligent control center must contain a variety of communication modules in order to achieve long-distance communication and control functions, expand the scope of use, and avoid the use limitations of the intelligent control center with a fixed form. As long as there is a network, the intelligent control center with a mobile form can control the intelligent devices, which shows the development direction of the future smart home system.

As a device that can independently carry out voice command recognition, user interaction, and instruction delivery, the intelligent control center in the mobile form also has a variety of modules, as shown in Table 4.2. First, there must be a powerful core control motherboard module to analyze various commands. The users can give orders through the touch panel module and transmit the processing information of the

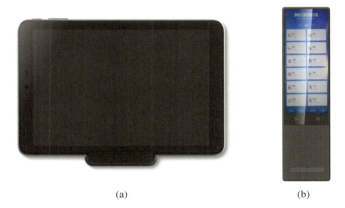

Figure 4.16 Two smart control centers of mobile terminals. (a) Tablet computer and (b) Intelligent remote control.

Table 4.2 Introduction of main modules and functions of the intelligent control center in a mobile form.

Serial number	Main modules	Function introduction
1	Core control motherboard module	Analyze and execute the operation commands of the intelligent control center and interact with other modules and external devices
2	Touch panel module	One of the main user interaction modules, two-way communication with the core control motherboard module, with the user touch interaction and display interaction and other functions
3	Voice acquisition module	One of the main user interaction modules, one-way communication with the core control motherboard module, to collect user voice commands
4	Cloud server module	Responsible for analyzing the user's voice commands and controlling the intelligent home appliances through the cloud-to-cloud docking mode
5	Infrared control module	Unidirectional communication with the core control motherboard module. Through the infrared remote control of home appliances control, achieve interactive function and improve the user's convenience
6	Network communication module	Bidirectional communication with the core control motherboard module. With the Internet docking, the intelligent control center can have access to the network

intelligent control center to the screen for the user to watch or the user's voice commands can be transmitted to the core control motherboard module through the voice acquisition module and then the core control motherboard module can be uploaded to the cloud server module for analysis and the required operations can be fed back to all modules. The process of the intelligent control center in the mobile form is basically the same as that of the intelligent control center with a fixed form.

4.2.4 *The future of the intelligent control center system*

In the current situation of scientific and technological development, intelligent control centers with both mobile and fixed forms can easily enter the users' homes and be integrated into the user's habits. However, due to the limitations of science and technology at the present stage, many modules of the intelligent control center are often relatively large and need to be integrated into larger devices, such as the intelligent control centers with a fixed form which are combined with the tea tables or the intelligent control center with the mobile form of a tablet computer. At the same time, because the power consumption of the equipment is often large, they need to be powered by a fixed power supply or built-in lithium battery. However, with the development of science and technology, the future electronic components will be greatly reduced, and power consumption will also be greatly reduced. With the future VR/AR technology, flexible material technology, 5G high-speed communication technology, high-capacity battery technology, and so on, there will be wearable intelligent control centers in the future. Wearable intelligent control centers, such as wristbands, would be worn by users. As soon as users raise their hands, they can issue commands through touch control or voice control through the wristbands. After analyzing user commands, the wristbands upload the corresponding commands to the cloud server through 5G technology, and the cloud server directly controls the relevant devices. In addition, users can control electrical appliances at home anytime and anywhere, and they can also view the real-time situation through the home security camera.

In the far future, with the maturity of the brain–computer interface technology, perhaps the intelligent control center system in the future can directly receive users' brain waves through wearable devices. Users can give instructions to electrical appliances as long as they think about commands without touching or speaking. In the era of advanced technology in the future, the intelligent control center system will be an essential product for everyone.

Bibliography

Bai Linfeng and Du Enlong (2018). Speech interaction technology reconstructs publishing. *Science-Technology and Publishing* (2): 49–53.

Chen Weibin (2017). Analysis of the development status and trend of "new retail". *Marketing Management Review* (3): 5.

Deng Yajing (2019). Brand upgrade, Skyworth Swaiot opens the era of large-screen AIoT. *Electrical* (4): 77.

Fan Qingyang (2016). *Design and Implementation of Cloud Based Intelligent Home System*. Changchun: Jilin University.

Gu Biling (2019). 5G key technologies and their impact on the Internet of Things. *Wireless Interconnection Technology* 16(07): 30–31.

Guo Lifang and Guo Chaofeng (2019). The trend of 5G catalyzed the rapid developing and landing VR/AR industry application. *China Telecommunications Trade* (4): 58–61.

Hu Wanting (2019). Research on smart home market demand and consumer identity in the era of AI. *Consumer Guide* (49): 2.

Huang Zhijie and Yu Guowei (2019). Analysis of the impact and development of 5G era on smart home. *Digital Space* (2): 17–18.

Ju Xinzhe (2019). 5G +8K wireless home entertainment new direction probe. *Telecom World* 26(10): 112–113.

Li Hui (2019). Suning: Boosting consumption upgrade with smart retail. *Guangming Daily*, 02–27 (10).

Li Xuelin (2018). Speech recognition based on human-computer interaction. *Electronics World* (21): 105.

Liu Jie, Wang Qingyang, and Lin Yilin (2018). Mobile VR application through the 5G network. *Communication Science* 34(10): 143–149.

Liu Lina (2011). Internet of Things leads the new life of smart home. *Intelligent Building and City Information* (2): 21–25.

Liu Ronghui, Peng Shiguo, and Liu Guoying (2014). Embedded speech recognition system based on intelligent home control. *Journal of Guangdong University of Technology* (2): 49–53.
Liu Xiao (2006). *Research on the Key Technology of Speech Recognition System*. Harbin: Harbin Engineering University.
Liu Xu (2016). Application and development of sensors in smart home. *Intelligent City* (11): 76.
Lu Yongxiang (2005). Challenges and opportunities for China's manufacturing industry in the 21st century. *Mechanical Engineer* (1): 9–13.
Meng Zhaosheng (2019). 5G smart park leading the industry tide. *Urban Development* (18): 24–25.
Peng Hongming (2012). *Research on the Architecture and Key Technology of Intelligent Home*. Beijing: Beijing Jiaotong University.
Qin Jingyan (2015). Large interaction design in the era of big data. *Packaging Engineering* 36(8): 1–5.
Ren Jun (2019). Development status and trend analysis of 8K UHDTV technology. *Video Engineering* 43(17): 11–13.
Shao Jun (2019). 5G opens the era of smart home. *Consumer Guide* (5): 41–43.
Tang Lei, Li Li, Sun Zhenzhong et al. (2019). Research on cloud platform technology architecture of furniture industry based on industrial Internet. *Furniture and Interior Decoration* (12): 71–76.
Tian Li (2011). Application of Internet of Things in smart home. *Communications and Information Technology* (02): 74–77.
Wang Guiying, Wang Xize, Yang Can et al. (2019). Innovative application of cloud office for 5G intelligent park. TD Industry Alliance, Mobile Communications. In *Proceedings of the 5G Network Innovation Symposium (2019)*. Guangzhou: Mobile Communications Magazine, pp. 344–349.
Wang Hua'an (2017). New technology promotes the innovation of smart home industry. *China Public Security* (6): 28–32.
Wang Jianing and Liu Wei (2016). The development of Internet of Things in the era of Big Data. *Telecom World*, 22(5): 52–53.
Wang Yajing and Zhang Yongyan (2019). Smart community management system based on 5G. *Electronic Technology and Software Engineering* (13): 5.
Wang Zhe, Li Yaqi, and Feng Xiaohui (2019). Development trend and outlook of AIoT field. *Artificial Intelligence View* (1): 10–18.
Wei An (2019). The 5G wisdom of community governance. *Decision-Making* (2): 46–49.
Xu Xiaoping and Lin Yu (2019). AI+ smart home technology and its trend. *Digital Communication World* (1): 65.
Xu Shuo and Mai Qiming (2011). Design and application of mobile phone network control system for smart home. *Mechanical and Electrical Technology* (3): 109–111.

You Xiaohu, Pan Zhiwen, Gao Xiqi *et al.* (2014). 5G mobile communication development trend and several key technologies. *Scientia Sinica Informationis* 44(05): 551–563.

Yu Shiping (2019). Application analysis of Internet of Things based on 5G mobile communication technology. *Electronics World* (3): 174–176.

Yue Jinghua (2014). *Research and Design of Smart Home System Based on Cloud Service*. Hangzhou: Hangzhou Dianzi University.

Zhang Yunyong (2019). 5G will fully enable the industrial Internet. *Communication Science* 35(1): 1–8.

Index

3D technology, 91
5G+ industrial Internet, 29, 31–35
5G+ intelligence, 36
5G+ IoT, 16–18
5G, v–vii, ix–xi, xiii–xv, 5–20, 25–27, 29, 31–40, 43, 47–48, 54–61, 63, 65–69, 72–75, 78, 80–88, 90, 94, 99, 111–113
5G access, 33–35, 43, 88
5G access, Wi-Fi 6, and Mesh, 82
5G and AIoT technologies, 90
5G base stations, 80, 86, 88
5G-based home networking devices, 78
5G-based smart homes, 18
5G-based STB, 84
5G broadband access, 43
5G channel, 54
5G cloud render technology, 73–74
5G collaboration, 31
5G communication technology, 69, 72
5G core network, 80–81, 87
5G customer premise equipment (5G CPE), 35, 40–41, 80–84
5G data, 10–15

5G elements, 32
5G era, xiii, 15–20, 25, 33, 39–40, 43, 48, 58–59, 61, 75, 77, 94, 98
5G high-speed communication technology, 123
5G mobile broadband, 39–40
5G mobile network, 71
5G mobile signals, 35
5G network access, 34, 67
5G network, 7, 10, 18, 34–35, 38, 59, 67, 71–72, 83–84, 86, 99
5G pipelines, 51–52
5G scene intelligence, 25
5G-related applications, 94
5G signal, 51, 66–67, 80–81, 86–88
5G signals and 5G base stations, 80
5G smart home, xiv, 14, 40, 99–100
5G standard-based services, 94
5G STB, 87–90
5G technology, vii, x–xi, xiv, 5, 10, 14–15, 18, 22, 25, 27, 34–35, 54–58, 60–61, 71–72, 74–75, 90–92, 97, 123
5G wireless access, 35, 82
5G wireless base station, 34–35
5G+ intelligent production, 36–37

A

AC + AP network access mode, 41
AC + AP topology, 41, 43
AC connection, 41
access equipment, 101
active scene intelligence, 26–27
AI + IoT, 17
AI algorithms, 48, 90, 96–97
AI chips, 93
AI image interaction technology, 7, 9
AI image quality enhancement technology, 103
AI image, 7, 9–10, 69, 103
AI intelligent speech technology, 7
AI speech and image recognition technology, 22
AI speech, 22, 66, 69
AI technology, 5–7, 60, 75, 90, 95
AI voice technology, 90
appliances
    home, 3–4, 16, 39, 96, 99, 110, 114, 117, 120, 122
    household, 3–4, 44, 47, 49–50, 111, 118–121
    intelligent electrical, 113
    intelligent home, 40, 57, 115, 122
    intelligent household, 100
    smart home, 39, 99
application scenarios, 6, 18–19, 46, 54, 56, 65, 105, 107
AR devices, 69–72, 74
artificial intelligence (AI) technology, 5–7, 53–55, 57, 60, 75, 90, 95, 100
artificial intelligence (AI), v, ix–x, 5–10, 21–22, 47–50, 53–61, 63, 65–66, 68–69, 75, 90, 93, 96–98, 100, 103, 108, 110–111
artificial intelligence Internet of Things (AIoT), 55, 65–68, 90–98, 115
AIoT applications, 94
AIoT ecological chain, 94
AIoT era, 92, 96
AIoT technology, 67, 90, 94, 97
AIoT-related scene-based services, 96
augmented reality (AR), 69–74, 123
automatic control, 3–4, 95

B

Big Data industry, 53
Big Data platforms, 94–95
Big Data scenarios, 52
Big Data technology scenarios, 53
Big Data, 6, 17, 21, 37, 47–49, 52–53, 56, 58–60, 94–95

C

centralized cloud computing, 101
cloud AI capabilities, 98
cloud computing center, 102
cloud computing, 98
cloud platform layer, 100, 102
cloud platform, 20–21, 50–52, 100, 102
cloud server, 17, 54, 104, 111, 119, 122–123
cloud services, 102
cloud technology, 6, 56
cloud-to-cloud docking, 122
commercial real estate, 54–56
control center of the home, 16
control center, 67, 107–108, 110, 112–114
control motherboard, 114–116, 118

D

data acquisition and transmission, 35
data acquisition technology, 10–15
data transmission, ix, 10, 15, 18–19, 33, 35, 75, 94
digital set-top boxes, 84
digital technology, 4, 58, 100

E

environmental monitoring sensors, 77
environmental sensing devices, 101
environmental sensor, 10, 14

H

home automation, 1, 4, 20, 95
home gateway, 16–17, 43, 83
home network access, 39
home network, 4, 39–41, 43, 45, 78–80, 100
home networking devices, 78–80
home security, 46, 74–77, 123

I

image sensors, 13–14
image technology, 7
industrial Internet platform, 31–35
industrial Internet, vi, xiii, 29, 31–32, 34
industrial network, 34
intelligent control center products, 112–113
intelligent control centers, 7, 40, 102, 111–123
intelligent devices, 16, 43, 50, 92, 114, 117–118, 120–121
intelligent equipment, 113
intelligent home devices, 118
intelligent home terminals, 44
intelligent interaction mode, 119
intelligent production lines, 31
intelligent products, 104
intelligent remote control technology, 103
intelligent remote controls, 103, 121
intelligent security, 101
intelligent speech, 7
interactive terminal, 74
interconnection and upward transmission of the data, 34
interconnection technology, 18–19, 100
Internet of Things (IoT), ix–x, 3, 6–7, 15–22, 44, 47–49, 52, 55–56, 58, 66, 90, 93–96, 99–100, 117
Internet of Things devices, 51, 65–66
Internet of Things (IoT) platform, 52, 102
Internet plus Advanced Manufacturing, 31
Internet technology, 55, 57
IoT technology, 2–3, 16, 55, 59, 75, 90

L

local control center, 104
long-distance wireless networks, 101

M

manufacturing basis, 29–30
manufacturing industry, xiii, 29–31, 35
manufacturing network, 34–35
Mesh CPE, 83
mobile communication, v–vi, ix, xi, xiii, 33, 39, 90
mobile Internet, vi, xiii, 6, 55–56, 90, 92
mobile signal access device, 35, 80
mobile VR/AR applications, 72
modern smart devices, 50
module
    5G, 66, 68, 82, 88–89
    built-in freezer, 114–115, 118–119
    built-in speaker, 114–117
    cloud server, 114, 118, 122
    core control motherboard, 114, 116–119, 121–122
    infrared control, 108, 110, 114, 117–118, 120, 122

network communication, 114, 116, 119, 122
touch panel, 114–116, 118, 121–122
voice acquisition, 114–115, 118, 122
wireless (Wi-Fi), 15, 82
wireless charging, 114–116

N
near-field communications, 101
network equipment, 18, 43, 78
network transmission, 31, 65
networkable devices, 45
new intelligent devices, 117

O
office and conference equipment, 101

P
passive scene intelligence, 26
personalized customization, 30
product intelligence, 20, 92

R
real-life scene design, 22
real-time communication, 16

S
scene
    AI kitchen, 110
    entertainment, 56, 114
    entry, 108
    fresh air, 110
    leisure, 110, 114
    meeting, 108
    movie, 108
    music, 107–108
    new retail, 59
    office, 110, 112, 114
    security, 111
    smart home, 55–57, 112
scene intelligence, 21–22, 25–27, 92

scene of the study, 107
scene-based services, 27, 92, 94, 96–98
security equipment, 75
security induction sensors, 77
sensor network, 14–15
sensor technology, 26, 98
sensors, 10–15, 21, 24–27, 55, 69, 75–78, 98, 108, 111, 117
smart device sensor technology, 26
smart devices, 6–7, 17, 19, 25, 40, 50–52, 65, 67, 69, 72, 90, 92, 96–97
smart home control solutions, 112
smart home devices, 6
smart home gateway, 43–47, 69, 78
smart home industry, 2–3, 20
smart home life, 3, 97
smart home manufacturing, 34–35
smart home market, 2–3
smart home networking, 16–17, 39, 41–42, 45
smart home platform, 45
smart home product, xiv, 2–3, 55, 69, 96
smart home scenario, 5, 15, 40–41
smart home technology, 55
smart home, xiv, 1–11, 13–18, 20–22, 25–27, 29–30, 32, 34–35, 39–47, 50, 53–57, 63, 67, 69, 74, 78, 94–97, 99–103, 105–108, 110–114
smart home-related products, 112
smart new retail, 58–60
smart office, ix, 108
smart product industry, 3
smart product, 2–3, 20–22, 25, 76, 95
smart real estate projects, 57
smart real estate, 54–57
smart retail, 58–59
smart sensors, 75–78
smart speaker, 16, 27, 46, 69, 97, 112
smart STB, 84–87

smart TV, 21, 46, 63, 65–68, 86
software platform, 55
system
    air conditioning, 103, 105–106
    AIoT, 92–94, 97–98
    data, 52–53
    device access, 51–52
    home security, 2, 75
    industrial Internet platform application, 35
    intelligent home, 99–101, 103
    intelligent security, 103, 105
    intelligent lighting, 103, 105–106
    intelligent office, 103–104
    IoT control s, 94–96
    IoT operating, 50
    IoT, 16, 20, 90, 92–95, 97–98
    modern home, 113
    operating s, 19, 48–51, 115
    smart eco, 57
    smart home, 4, 13, 56, 74, 99–103, 106, 108, 110, 113–114, 121
    super TV, 103

T

techniques of artificial intelligence, 53
technological transformation, 30
technology transformation and upgrade, 55
terminal devices, 19, 74, 101
terminal, 16, 18–20, 35, 43, 45–46, 48, 53–54, 74, 83–84, 93, 96–97, 100–101, 105

the mobile form of the intelligent control center, 120–121
touch operation, 119

U

user interaction, 121–122

V

virtual reality (VR), 69–74, 123
visual Big Data platform, 94–95
visual Big Data, 94
voice command operation, 119
voice command recognition, 121
voice recognition technology, 7, 48, 103
VR device, 69–70, 74
VR industry chain, 71
VR industry, 71, 74
VR technology, 69
VR/AR content service, 74
VR/AR content, 73

W

wearable intelligent control centers, 123
Wi-Fi 6, 19, 82–83
Wi-Fi connection, 40, 43, 47, 83
Wi-Fi Mesh, 82–83
Wi-Fi signals, 35, 67, 80
Wi-Fi wireless network interfaces, 80
Wi-Fi, 3, 6, 10, 18–19, 35, 40–43, 45, 65–69, 72, 75, 83, 101, 116
wireless (Wi-Fi) connections, 43
wireless data communication, 117
wireless sensor network, 14–15